it all begins
with an idea...

25

american
showcase

and collaboration

Accepting an illustration commission is accepting a collaboration between the artist and the art director. When I worked as an editorial art director, this usually consisted of me sending manuscripts to illustrators and leaving them alone to interpret it as art. My contributions were selecting the appropriate illustrators, letting them know the fee, deadline and specs, and then framing the results properly in the magazine. That's probably understating it some, but not much. That kind of assignment still comes around now and then, but comparatively infrequently.

Today, the collaboration is much more involved. I think that one of the skills an illustrator needs to develop is the ability to discern what the client truly needs. Although at times it can be confusing and even frustrating, still, the business of making images for reproduction is more challenging and ultimately more satisfying than anything I've engaged in during my career.

DUGALD STERMER,
who is featured on our 25th Anniversary cover

President and Publisher **IRA SHAPIRO**
Executive Vice President **ANN MIDDLEBROOK**
Controller **BRENDA MASSY**
Director of Sales and Marketing **ERICA STURDEVANT**
Director of Production **STANLEY REDFERN**
Director of Design **JILL BLUMING**

ADVERTISING SALES
Client Services Manager **RANDY PUDDU**
Sales Coordinator **CLAIRE MISSANELLI**
Sales Representatives **RITA ALLEN, JO ANN MILLER, DAVE TABLER**

CREATIVE
Designer **JOHN TROCHE**
Junior Designer **JAMES DAHER**

PRODUCTION
Production/Client Relations Manager **CHUCK ROSENOW**
Production Coordinator **JUSTINE KEEFE**
Traffic Coordinator **CURT SWEDIN**
Assistant Traffic Coordinator **EDSON AVELAR**

DISTRIBUTION
Distribution Manager **JAMES KRAVITZ**
Labels To Go Coordinator **KAREN WRIGHT**
Distribution Assistant **THERESA AFFUSO**

ADMINISTRATION
Office Manager **JACQUELINE ILDEFONSO**
Senior Accounting Assistant **MICHELLE ROBERTS**
Accounting Assistant **ALEXANDRIA MANIATAKIS**
Digital Communications Consultant **JASON ELLIS**
Receptionist **ROSALEE ELLIS**

Book Design **DAN DYKSEN**
Front Cover Illustration **DUGALD STERMER**

Special Thanks to Sally Heflin

U.S. and Canada Book Trade Distributor and Publisher American Showcase, Inc. 915 Broadway, 14th Floor New York, NY 10010 Tel 212.673.6600 or 800.894.7469
Fax 212.673.9795 email info@amshow.com url www.americanshowcase.com

For Sales Outside the U.S. and Canada AVA Distribution SA 56a Chapel Road Worthing, West Sussex BN11 1DQ United Kingdom Tel 44 1903 204495 Fax 44 1903 204499

Color Separation PrintPro Ltd., Hong Kong

Printing and Manufacturing Tien Wah Press (PTE) Limited, Singapore

American Illustration Showcase 25 BOOK 1 of 2 ISBN 1-887-165-39-8 ISSN 0278-8128

showcase **illustration**

25

contents

representatives

KENNY KIERNAN
ILLUSTRATION

CHARLIE HILL

Sam Ward

MENDOLA LTD

Sam Ward

MENDOLA LTD   view online portfolios at WWW.MENDOLAART.COM

420 LEXINGTON AVENUE NEW YORK, NY 10170   TELEPHONE 212.986.5680   FAX 212.818.1246   EMAIL mendolaart@aol.com
Editorial: 941.346.7772

JIM TALBOT

MENDOLA LTD

420 LEXINGTON AVENUE
NEW YORK, NY 10170.
TELEPHONE 212.986.5680

WWW.MENDOLAART.COM

SUPER FUNHOUSE
STEP RIGHT UP...FOR FUN!

COLLECT ALL 4

CIRCUS MAZE

FUN HOUSE TWISTER

BUMPER CAR BONANZA

MENTAL BLOCK CHALLENGE

99¢ EACH

Pizza Hut

REPRESENTED BY

MENDOLA ARTISTS
GRAYBAR BUILDING
420 LEXINGTON AVENUE
PENTHOUSE 10170 NEW YORK NY USA
TEL: 212 986 5680   FAX: 212 818 1246

www.rowanbarnes-murphy.com

MIKE WIMMER – I DO ART INC.

3905 Nicole Circle, Norman, OK 73072 405-329-0478 Web Site: Mikewimmer.com

Tom Newsom

Tom Newsom

Liisa Chauncy Guida
AND
MENDOLA LTD
420 LEXINGTON AVENUE
NEW YORK, NY 10170

GARRY COLBY

MacDonalds' Fun Times

MARILEE HEYER

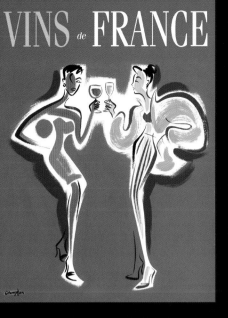

VINS de FRANCE

CORONA

Corona
Light
IMPORTED BEER FROM MEXICO

Corona
Light

Corona
Extra
LA CERVEZA MAS FINA
IMPORTED BEER FROM MEXICO

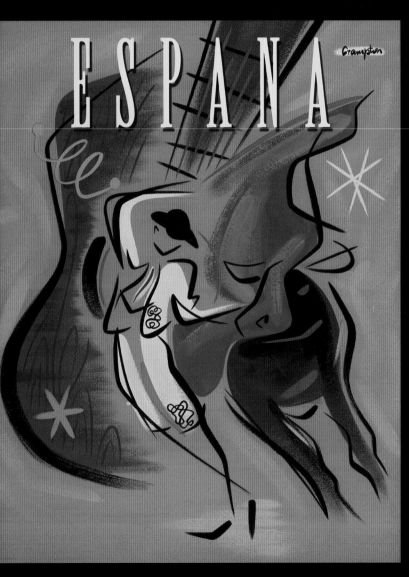

ESPANA

Crampton

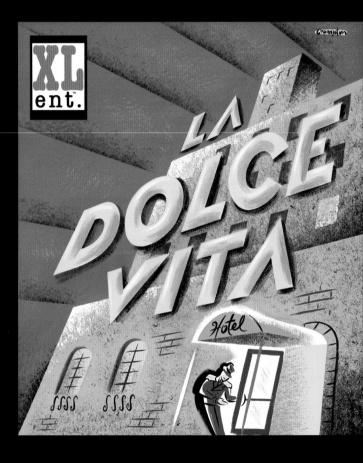

XL
ent.

LA
DOLCE
VITA

Hotel

crampton
michael

www.mcrampton.com

Jeffrey Mangiat

Jeffrey Mangiat

BORIS ZLOTSKY

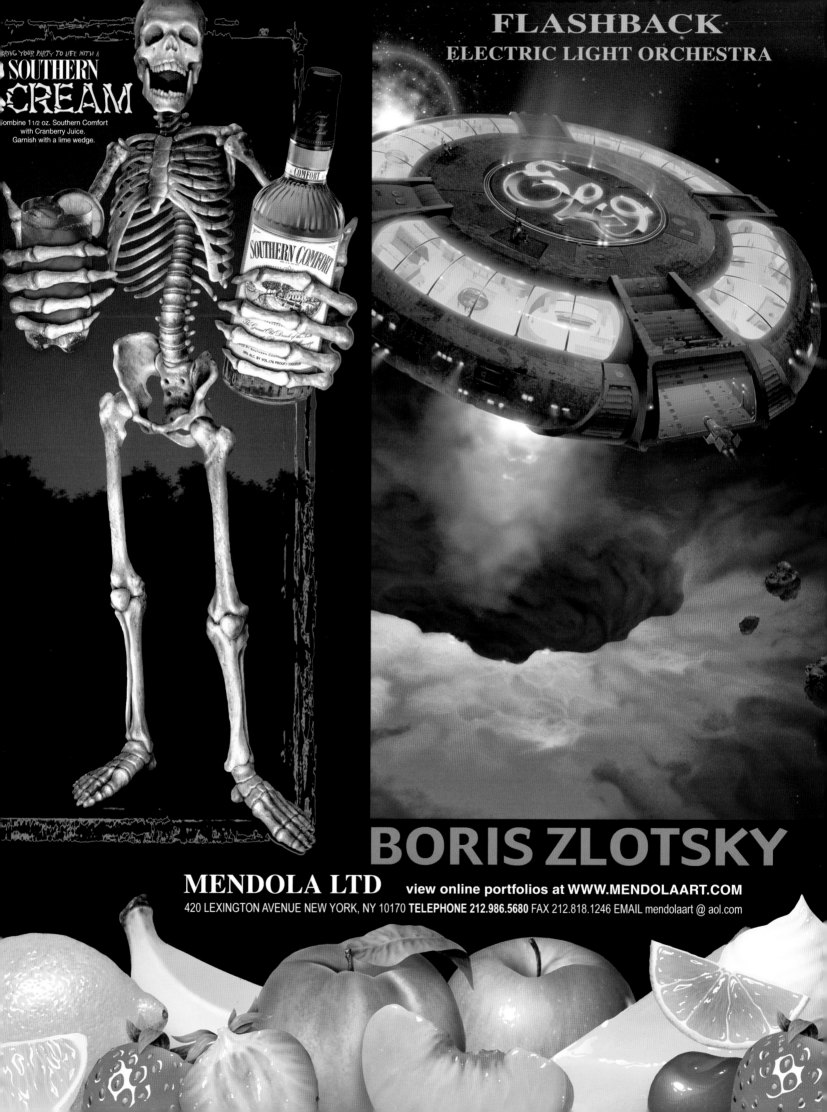

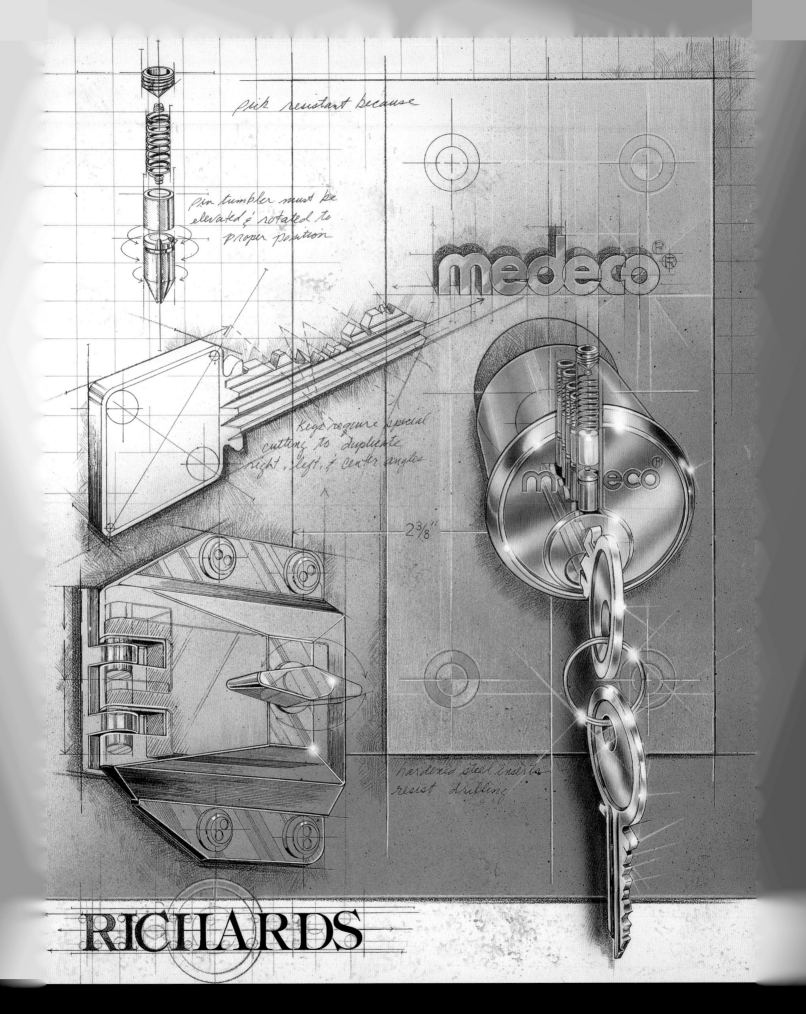

pick resistant because

pin tumbler must be
elevated & rotated to
proper position

medeco®

Keys require special
cutting to duplicate
right, left, & center angles

2 3/8"

hardened steel inserts
resist drilling

RICHARDS

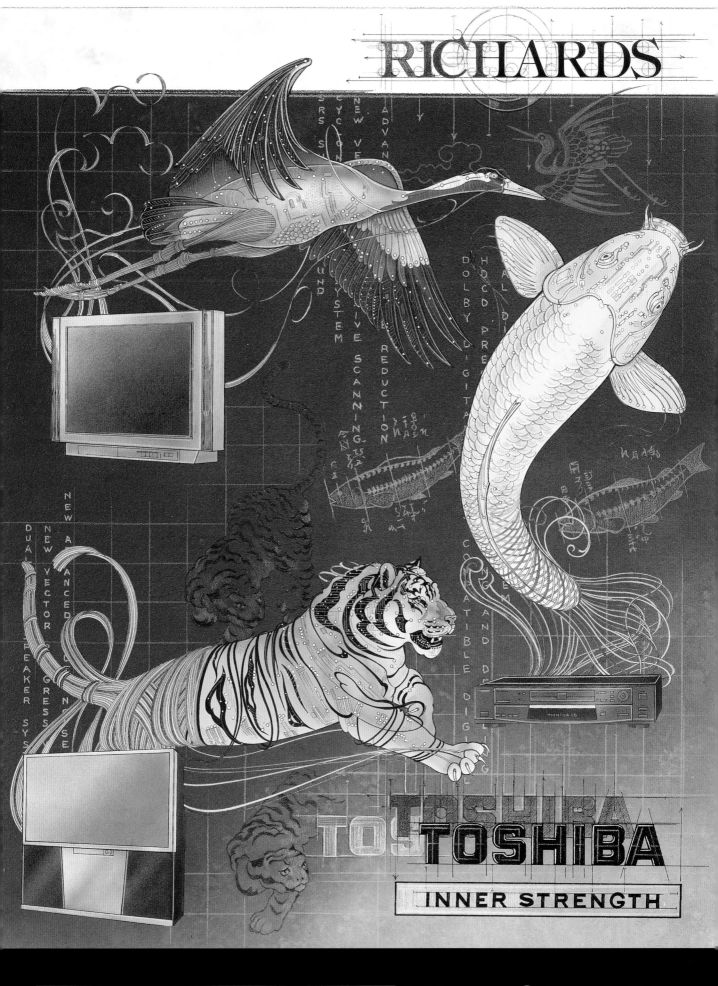

RICHARDS

TOSHIBA
INNER STRENGTH

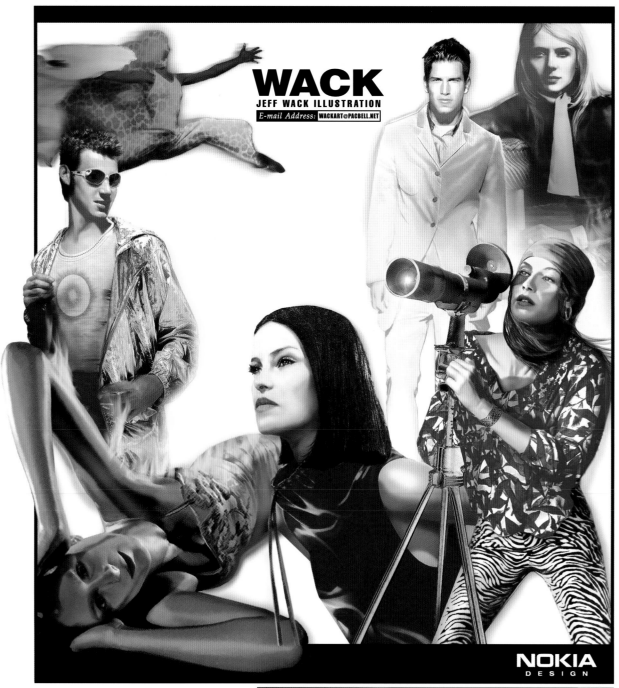

WACK
JEFF WACK ILLUSTRATION
E-mail Address: WACKART@PACBELL.NET

NOKIA
DESIGN

David
SCHLEINKOFER

MENDOLA LTD

420 LEXINGTON AVENUE
NEW YORK, NY 10170
TELEPHONE 212.986.5680
FAX 212.818.1246
EMAIL mendolaart@aol.com
view online portfolios at

WWW.MENDOLAART.COM

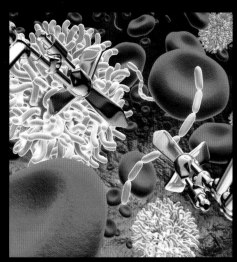

SANDBOX DIGITAL PLAYGROUND

3D IMAGING / MULTIMEDIA / ILLUSTRATION / WEB ART / ANIMATION
www.sandboxdp.com / MENDOLA LTD / 212 / 986 / 5680 / www.mendolaart.com

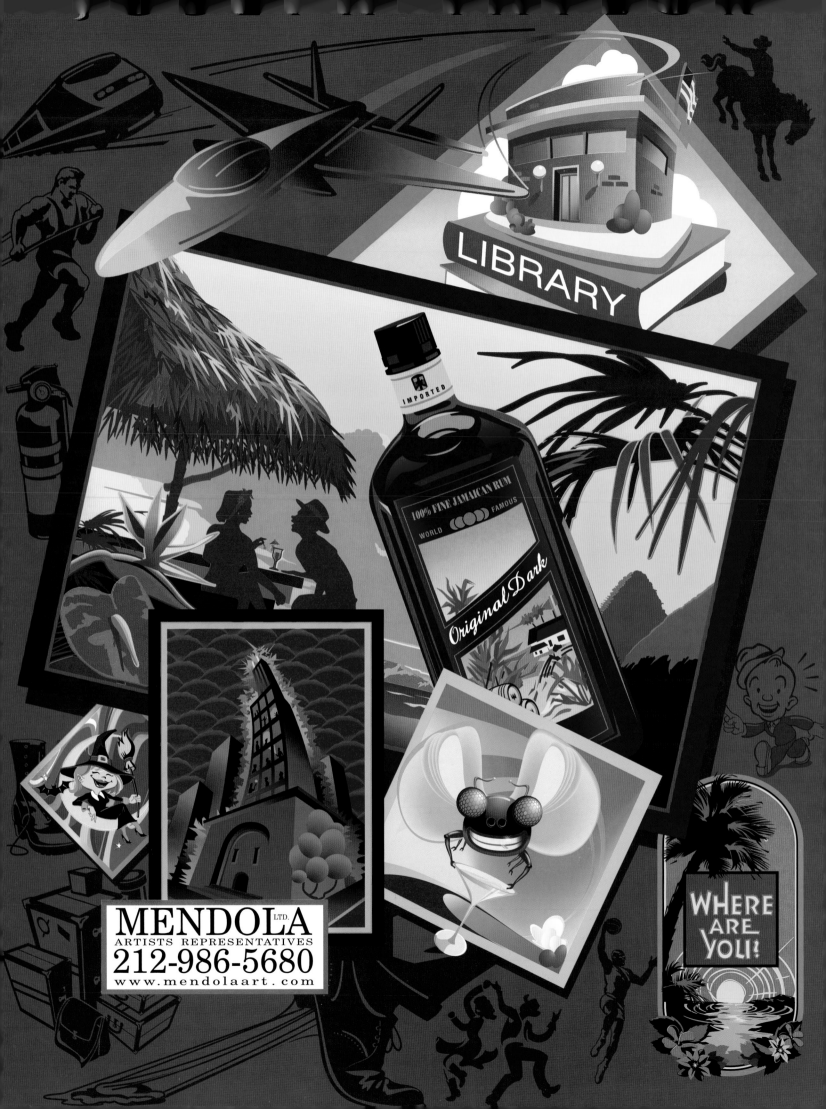

MICK MCGINTY

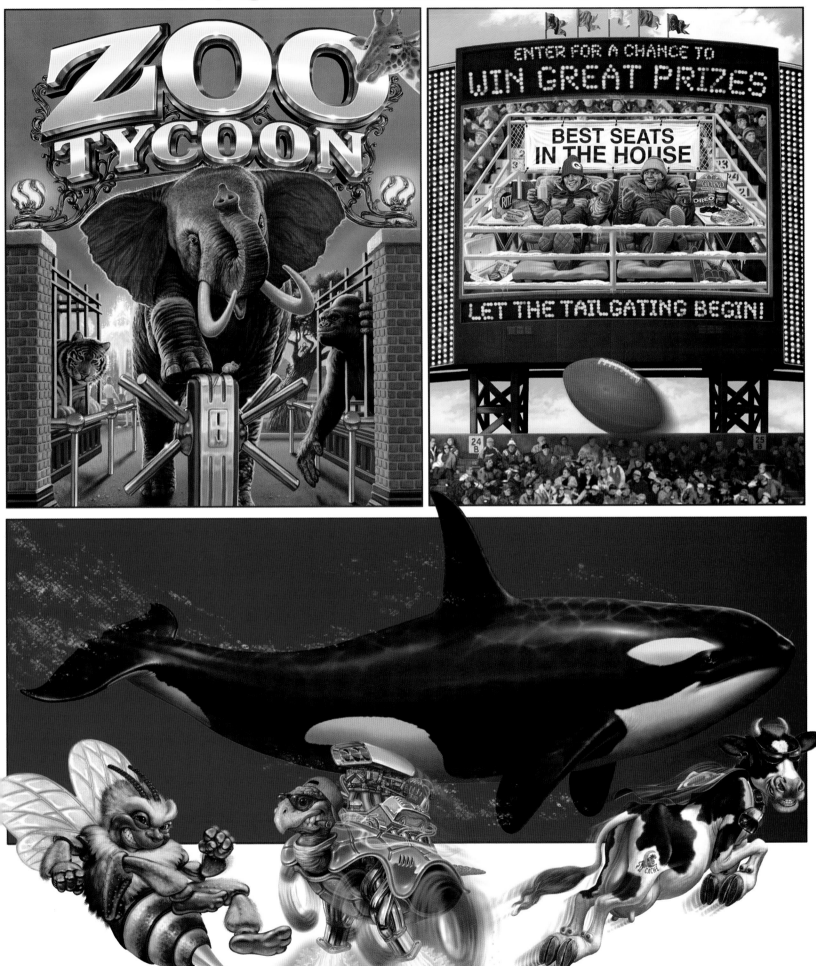

53

Sean Parkes

HUMOROUS ILLUSTRATOR

Represented by **MENDOLA LTD.**
420 Lexington Avenue, New York, N.Y. 10170
Ph: 212-986-5680 Fx: 212-818-1246

EAST
BAY
STUDIO

MENDOLA ARTISTS
212.986.5680
Fax 818.1246
mendolaart@aol.com

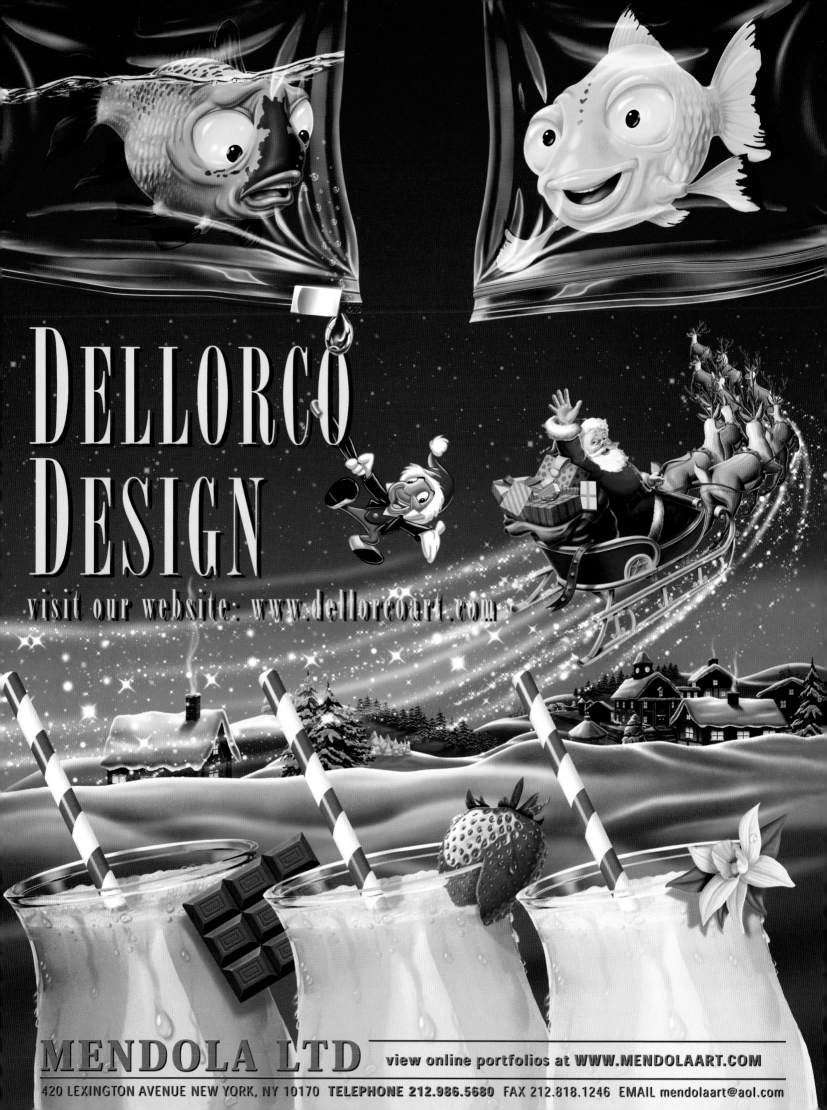

denise fraifeld

mendola artists

HEIDI SCHMIDT

www.heidischmidt.com

CALIFORNIA ORANGES
PictSweet

SELECTED FROM 100% NAVEL ORANGES, OJAI CALIFORNIA

MENDOLA LTD

420 LEXINGTON AVENUE NEW YORK, NY 10170 **TELEPHONE 212.986.5680** FAX 212.818.1246 EMAIL mendolaart@aol.com **WWW.MENDOLAART.COM**

ROBERT HYNES

Dave Henderson

Christopher Nick

NOTARILE

ILLUSTRATOR

Robert Tanenbaum

THINGS YOU FIND AT A SUPER BOWL PARTY

1. The Armchair Quarterback
2. Mourning a Recent Loss
3. Late and Empty-handed Guests
4. Prefers Watching the Commercials
5. The Nature Lover
6. Nature
7. The Pizza Delivery Guy
8. Still Talking About the Election
9. The Fumble
10. The Failed Hors d'Oeuvre
11. Coca-Cola
12. Vase, Ming Dynasty, 14th Century

Coca-Cola

www.enjoy-the-game.com

© 2000 The Coca-Cola Company. "Coca-Cola." is a registered trademark of the Coca-Cola Company. "Super Bowl" and the Super Bowl XXXV logo are registered trademarks of the National Football League.

MENDOLA LTD
view online portfolios at WWW.MENDOLAART.COM

420 LEXINGTON AVENUE NEW YORK, NY 10170 **TELEPHONE 212.986.5680** FAX 212.818.1246 EMAIL mendolaart@aol.com

STEVE CHORNEY

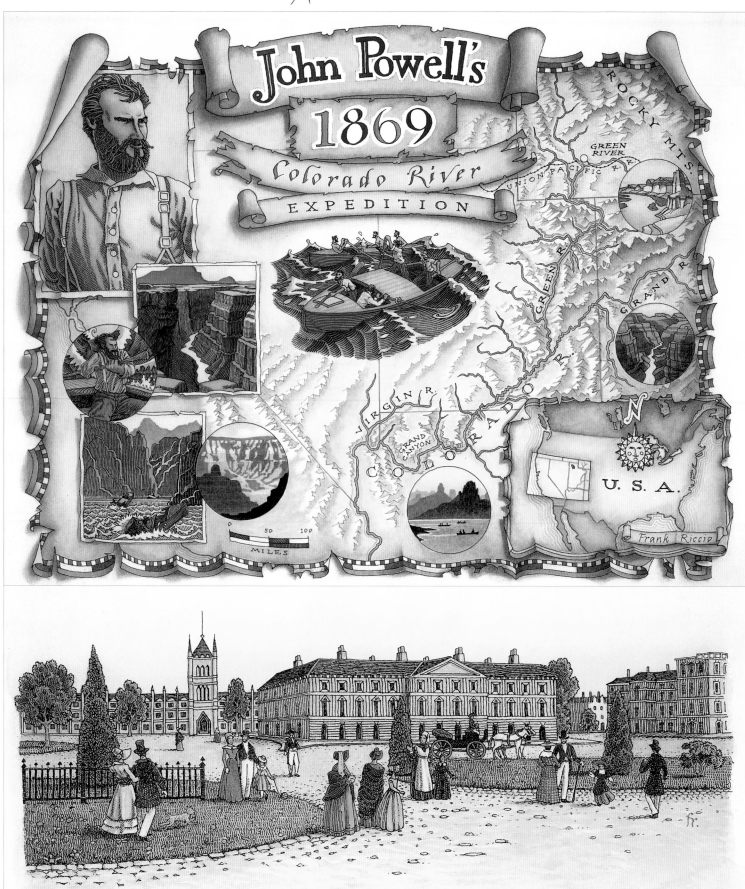

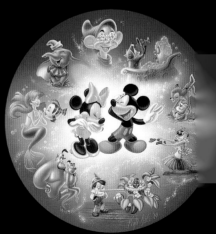

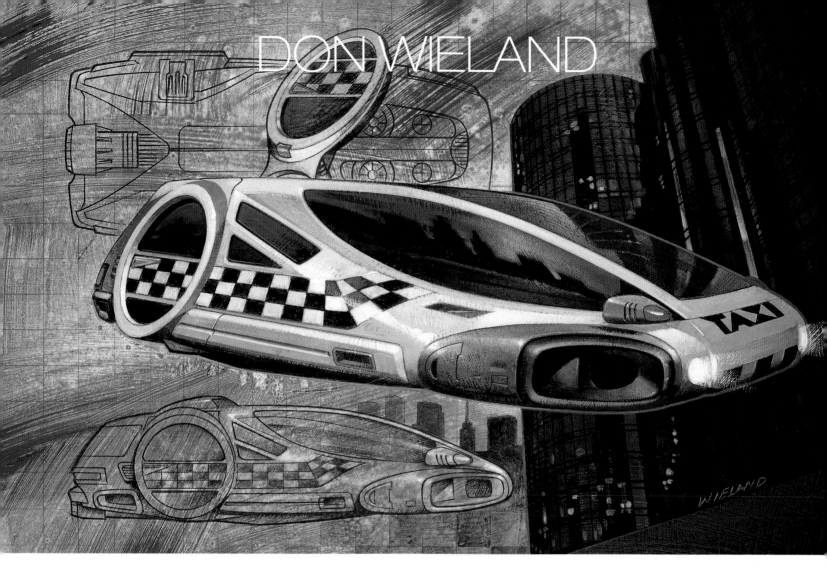

DON WIELAND

ROBERT
KROGLE

COVER ART FROM STAR WARS HARDBACK - RANDOM HOUSE

PACKAGE DESIGN - ACTION MAN GAME BOX TOP ART - HASBRO GAMES

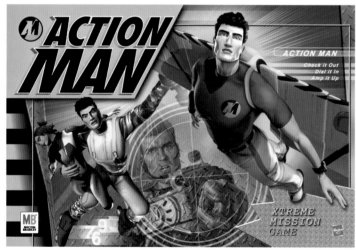

22 INCH PUZZLE & PUZZLE TIN ILLUSTRATION - HASBRO GAMES

Steve Anderson

sande70668@aol.com

Sharon Kurlansky Associates / *artists' representatives*   t: 508 872-4549   f: 508 480-9221
e: skurlan@charter.net   w: blairthornley.com   w: laughing-stock.com

BlairThornley

10:10
Rue Scribe

Rue St. du Faubourg
Honore
11:30

METRO

Rue de la
1:10 pompe

Galerie
Vivienne
1:40

Beth Adams

www.theispot.com/artist/adams

Represented by Gerald & Cullen Rapp
108 East 35th St., New York, N.Y. 10016
(212) 889-3337, fax (212) 889 3341

Beth Adams

www.theispot.com/artist/adams

Represented by Jerald & Cullen Rapp
108 East 35th St., New York, N.Y. 10016
(212) 889-3337, fax (212) 889 3341

Gerald & Cullen Rapp, Inc.
108 East 35 St., New York, NY 10016
Ph: (212) 889-3337 Fax (212) 889-3341
www.theispot.com/artist/anderson

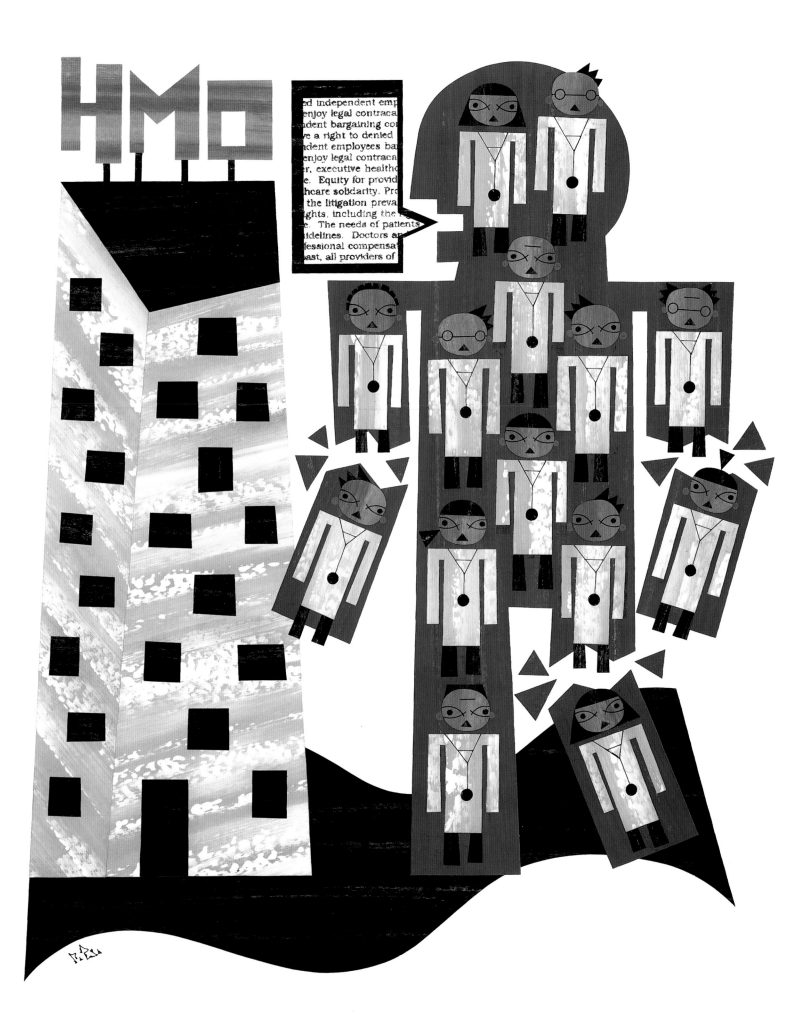

Philip Anderson

Gerald & Cullen Rapp, Inc.
108 East 35 St., New York, NY 10016
Ph: (212) 889-3337 Fax (212) 889-3341
www.theispot.com/artist/anderson

Stuart Briers

Gerald & Cullen Rapp, Inc.
108 East 35 St., New York, NY 10016
Ph: (212) 889-3337 Fax (212) 889-3341
www.theispot.com/artist/briers
www.stuartbriers.com

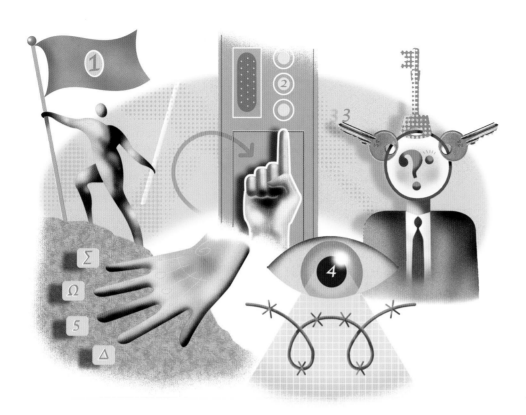

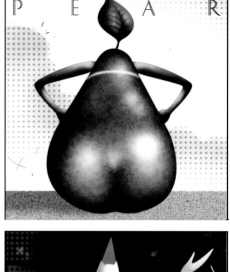

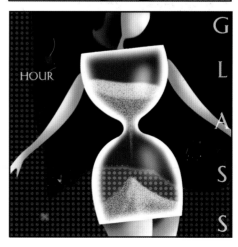

Stuart Briers

Gerald & Cullen Rapp, Inc.
108 East 35 St., New York, NY 10016
Ph: (212) 889-3337 Fax (212) 889-3341
www.theispot.com/artist/briers
www.stuartbriers.com

Lonnie Busch

Gerald & Cullen Rapp, Inc.
108 East 35 St., New York, NY 10016
Ph: (212) 889-3337 Fax (212) 889-3341
www.theispot.com/artist/busch

Lonnie Busch

Gerald & Cullen Rapp, Inc.
108 East 35 St., New York, NY 10016
Ph: (212) 889-3337 Fax (212) 889-3341
www.theispot.com/artist/busch

Jonathan Carlson

Gerald & Cullen Rapp, Inc.

108 East 35th Street
New York, NY 10016
Phone: (212) 889-3337
Fax: (212) 889-3341
www.theispot.com/artist/carlson

Jonathan Carlson

Gerald & Cullen Rapp, Inc.

108 East 35th Street
New York, NY 10016
Phone: (212) 889-3337
Fax: (212) 889-3341
www.theispot.com/artist/carlson

Jack Davis

Gerald & Cullen Rapp, Inc.
108 East 35 St., New York, NY 10016
Ph: (212) 889-3337 Fax (212) 889-3341
www.theispot.com/artist/davis

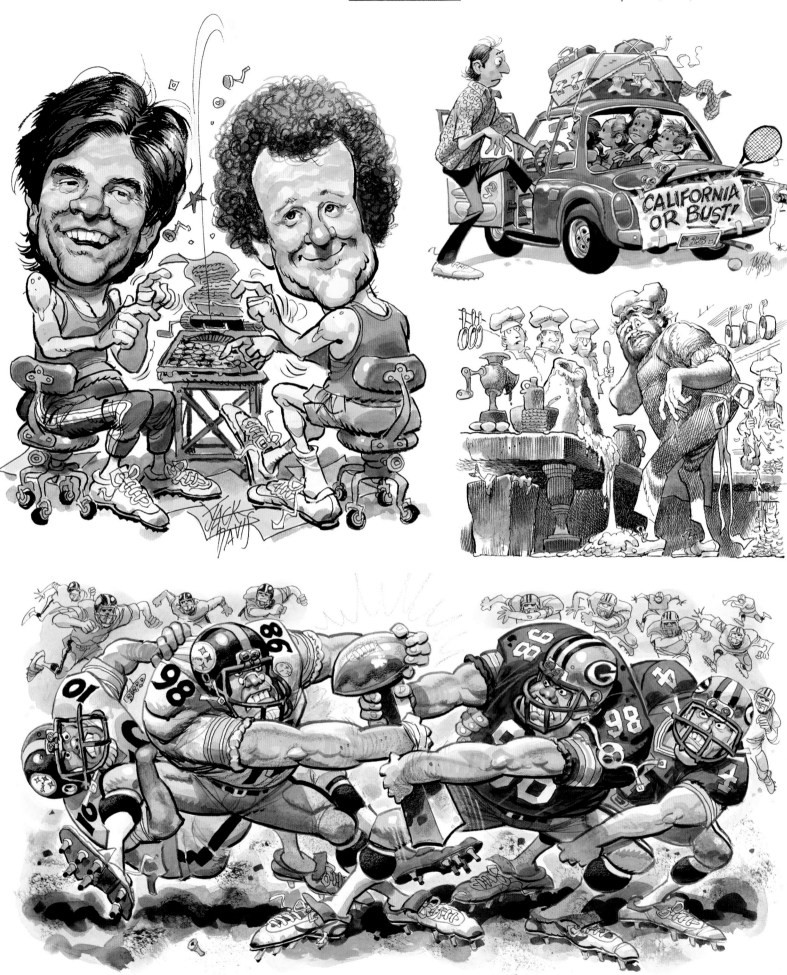

Jack Davis

Gerald & Cullen Rapp, Inc.
108 East 35 St., New York, NY 10016
Ph: (212) 889-3337 Fax (212) 889-3341
www.theispot.com/artist/davis

Gerald & Cullen Rapp, Inc.
108 East 35 St., New York, NY 10016
Ph: (212) 889-3337 Fax (212) 889-3341
www.theispot.com/artist/demichiell

Robert deMichiell

Gerald & Cullen Rapp, Inc.
108 East 35 St., New York, NY 10016
Ph: (212) 889-3337 Fax (212) 889-3341
www.theispot.com/artist/demichiell

Leo Espinosa

Represented by Gerald & Cullen Rapp, Inc. | P 212 889 3337 | F 212 889 3341 | www.theispot.com/artist/espinosa

Mark Fredrickson

Gerald & Cullen Rapp, Inc.
108 East 35 St., New York, NY 10016
Ph: (212) 889-3337 Fax (212) 889-3341
www.theispot.com/artist/fredrickson

Mark Fredrickson

Gerald & Cullen Rapp, Inc.
108 East 35 St., New York, NY 10016
Ph: (212) 889-3337 Fax (212) 889-3341
www.theispot.com/artist/fredrickson

CHRIS GALL

Gerald and Cullen Rapp, Inc.
108 East 35 St., New York, NY 10016
Ph: (212) 889-3337 Fax (212) 229-3341
www.theispot.com/artist/cgall
www.chrisgall.com

Gerald and Cullen Rapp, Inc.
108 East 35 St., New York, NY 10016
Ph: (212) 889-3337 Fax (212) 229-3341
www.theispot.com/artist/cgall
www.chrisgall.com

CHRIS GALL

Gerald & Cullen Rapp, Inc.
108 East 35 St., New York, NY 10016
Ph: (212) 889-3337 Fax (212) 889-3341
www.theispot.com/artist/ggreif

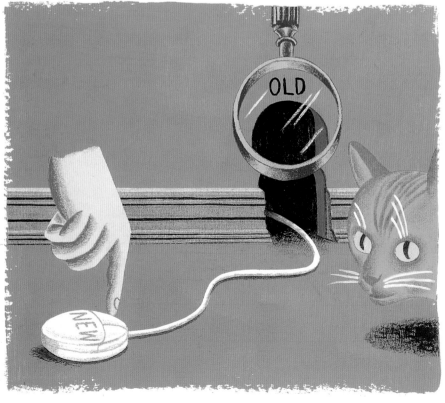

Gene Greif

Gerald & Cullen Rapp, Inc.
108 East 35 St., New York, NY 10016
Ph: (212) 889-3337 Fax (212) 889-3341
www.theispot.com/artist/ggreif

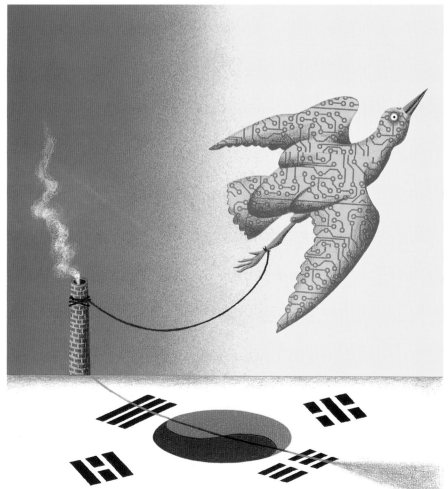

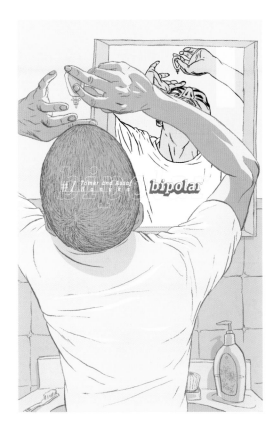

Tomer Hanuka

Gerald & Cullen Rapp, Inc.
108 East 35 St., New York, NY 10016
Ph: (212) 889-3337 Fax (212) 889-3341
www.theispot.com/artist/hanuka

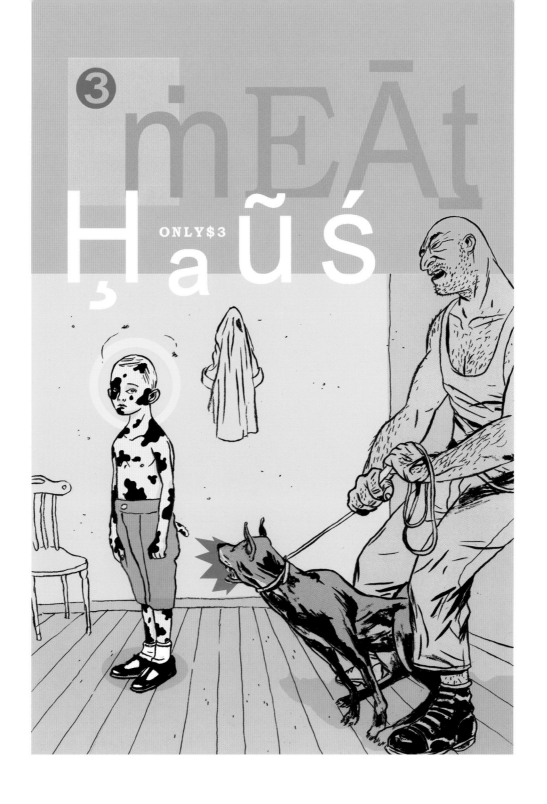

③ mEĀt

HₐũŚ

ONLY$3

Tomer Hanuka

Gerald & Cullen Rapp, Inc.
108 East 35 St., New York, NY 10016
Ph: (212) 889-3337 Fax (212) 889-3341
www.theispot.com/artist/hanuka

Peter Horjus

Gerald & Cullen Rapp, Inc.
108 East 35 St., New York, NY 10016
Ph: (212) 889-3337 Fax (212) 889-3341
www.theispot.com/artist/horjus

Illustrations are Adobe Illustrator EPS files and can be conveniently emailed :)

Peter Horjus

Gerald & Cullen Rapp, Inc.
108 East 35 St., New York, NY 10016
Ph: (212) 889-3337 Fax (212) 889-3341
www.theispot.com/artist/horjus

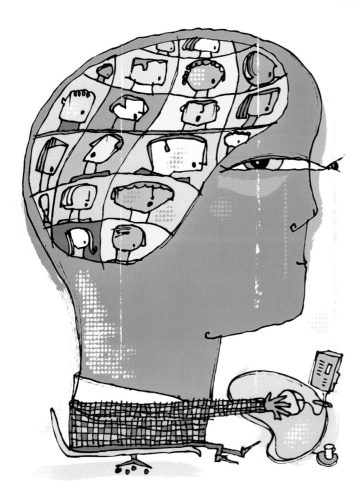

peter horvath

gerald & cullen rapp inc. 108 east 35th street new york, ny. 10016
phone 212-889-3337 / fax 212-889-3341 / www.theispot.com/artist/phorvath

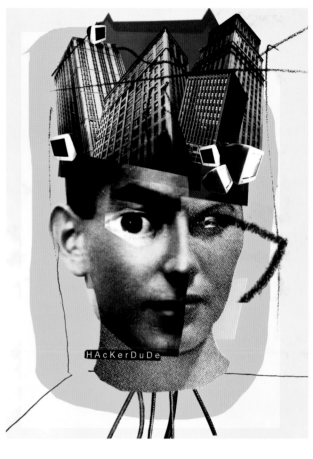

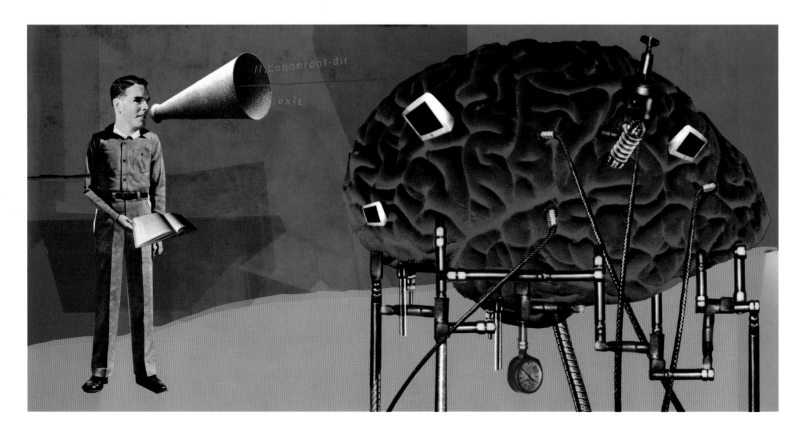

horváth,

SEND

CELIA JOHNSON ILLUSTRATION www.cprojex.com

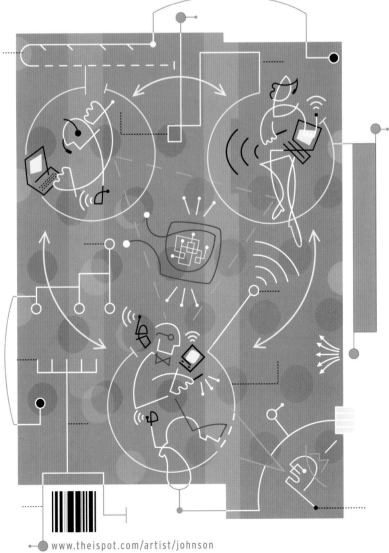

REPRESENTED BY GERALD & CULLEN RAPP, INC.

T 212 889 3337
F 212 889 3341

CELIA JOHNSON ILLUSTRATION

Douglas B. Jones

GERALD & CULLEN RAPP, INC
108 East 35th St., New York, NY 1001
ph: 212-889-3337 fax: 212-889-334
www.theispot.com/artist/jone
www.douglasbjones.co

Douglas B. Jones

GERALD & CULLEN RAPP, INC.
108 East 35th St., New York, NY 10016
ph: 212-889-3337 fax: 212-889-3341
www.theispot.com/artist/jones
www.douglasbjones.com

NEWS TO YOU

digital delivery!

GERALD & CULLEN RAPP, INC.
108 EAST 35 ST., NEW YORK, NY 10016
PH: 212 889 3337 FAX: 212 889 3341
WWW.THEISPOT.COM/ARTIST/KACZMAN

JAMES KACZMAN

GERALD & CULLEN RAPP, INC.
108 EAST 35 ST., NEW YORK, NY 10016
PH: 212 889 3337 FAX: 212 889 3341
WWW.THEISPOT.COM/ARTIST/KACZMAN

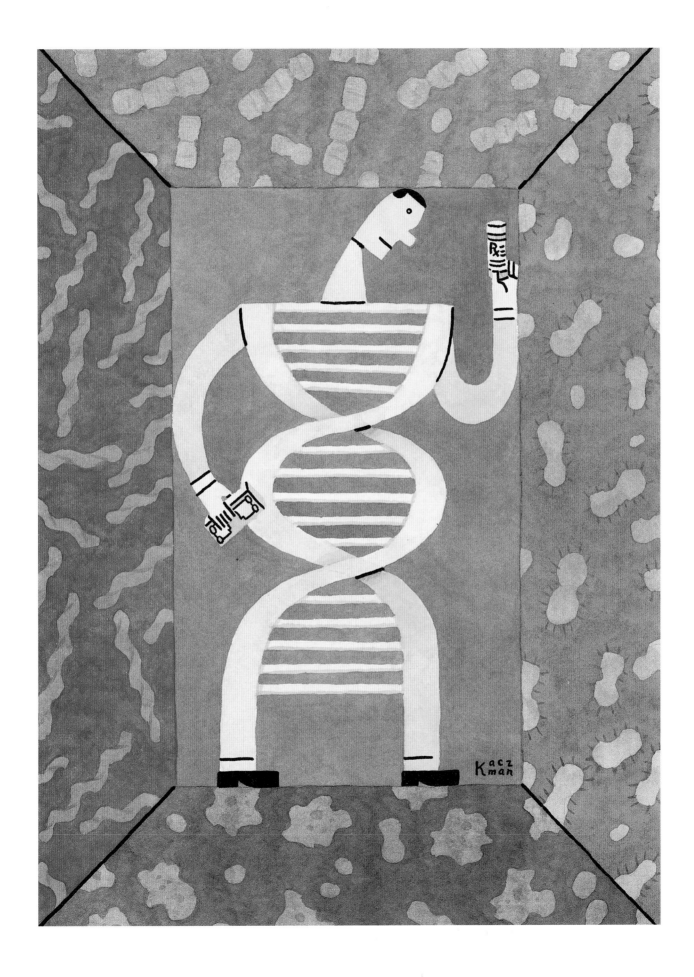

STEVE KELLER

digital

Gerald & Cullen Rapp, Inc.
108 East 35 St., New York, NY 10016
Ph: (212) 889-3337 Fax (212) 889-3341
www.theispot.com/artist/keller

www.drizzle.com/~stevek

STEVE KELLER
digital

Gerald & Cullen Rapp, Inc.
108 East 35 St., New York, NY 10016
Ph: (212) 889-3337 Fax (212) 889-3341
www.theispot.com/artist/keller

$$E = MC^2$$

www.drizzle.com/~stevek

Gerald & Cullen Rapp, Inc.
Phone: (212) 889-3337
Fax: (212) 889-3341
www.theispot.com/artist/jdking

J.D. KING

Gerald & Cullen Rapp, Inc.

108 East 35th Street
New York, NY 10016
Phone: (212) 889-3337
Fax: (212) 889-3341
www.theispot.com/artist/jdking

Gerald & Cullen Rapp, Inc.
108 East 35 St., New York, NY 10016
Ph: (212) 889-3337 Fax (212) 889-3341
www.theispot.com/artist/kubinyi

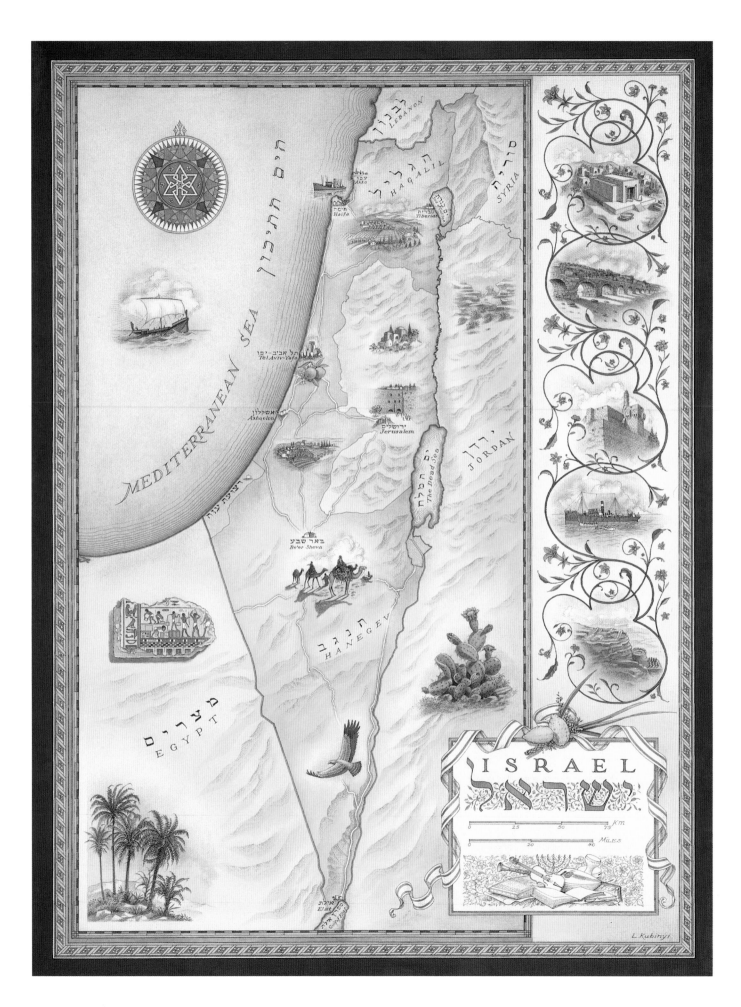

Laszlo Kubinyi

Gerald & Cullen Rapp, Inc.
108 East 35 St., New York, NY 10016
Ph: (212) 889-3337 Fax (212) 889-3341
www.theispot.com/artist/kubinyi

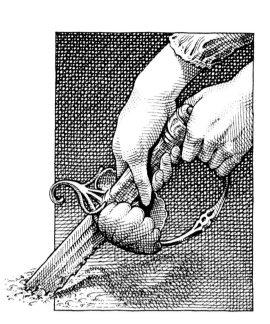

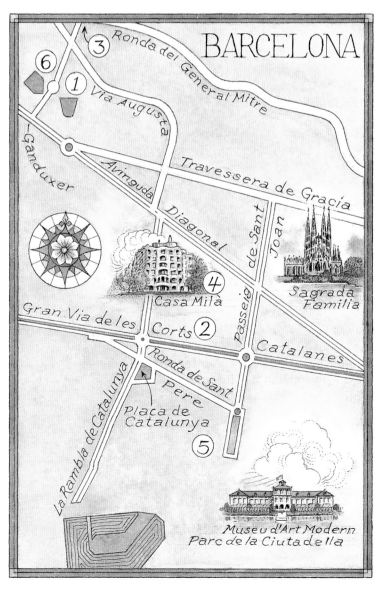

SCOTT LAUMANN

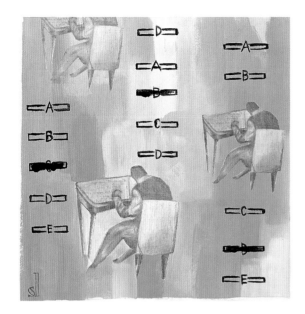

SCOTT LAUMANN

Gerald & Cullen Rapp
108 East 35th St.
New York, NY 10016
P 212.889.3337 F 212-889-3341
www.theispot.com/artist/laumann
WWW.SCOTTLAUMANN.COM

115

Gerald & Cullen Rapp, Inc

108 East 35 St. , New York, NY 10016
Ph: (212) 889-3337 Fax (212) 889-334
www.theispot.com/artist/liu

Gerald & Cullen Rapp, Inc

108 East 35 St. , New York, NY 10016
Ph: (212) 889-3337 Fax (212) 889-3341
www.theispot.com/artist/liu

www.davyliu.com

Brian Lovenduski

Gerald & Cullen Rapp, Inc.
108 East 35 St., New York, NY 10016
Ph: (212) 889-3337 Fax (212) 889-3341
www.theispot.com/artist/blovenduski

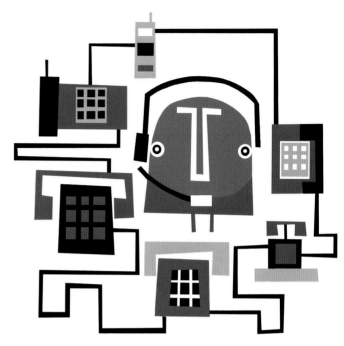

Brian Lovenduski

Gerald & Cullen Rapp, Inc.
108 East 35 St., New York, NY 10016
Ph: (212) 889-3337 Fax (212) 889-3341
www.theispot.com/artist/blovenduski

HAL Mayforth

GERALD & CULLEN RAPP, INC.
108 E. 35TH ST. NY, NY 10016
P. 212·889·3337 F. 212·889·3341
www.theispot.com/artist/mayforth
www.mayforth.com

mayforth.com

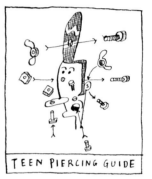

TEEN PIERCING GUIDE

HAL Mayforth

GERALD & CULLEN RAPP, INC.
108 E. 35 TH ST. NY, NY 10016
P. 212·889·3337 F. 212·889·3341
www.theispot.com/artist/mayforth
www.mayforth.com

Aaron Meshon

Gerald & Cullen Rapp, Inc.
108 East 35 St., New York, NY 10016
Ph: (212) 889-3337 Fax (212) 889-3341
www.theispot.com/artist/ameshon

Aaron Meshon

Gerald & Cullen Rapp, Inc.
108 East 35 St., New York, NY 10016
Ph: (212) 889-3337 Fax (212) 889-3341
www.theispot.com/artist/ameshon

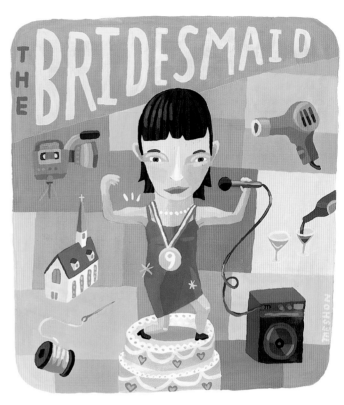

Bruce Morser

Gerald & Cullen Rapp, Inc.
108 East 35 St., New York, NY 10016
Ph: (212) 889-3337 Fax (212) 889-3341
www.theispot.com/artist/morser

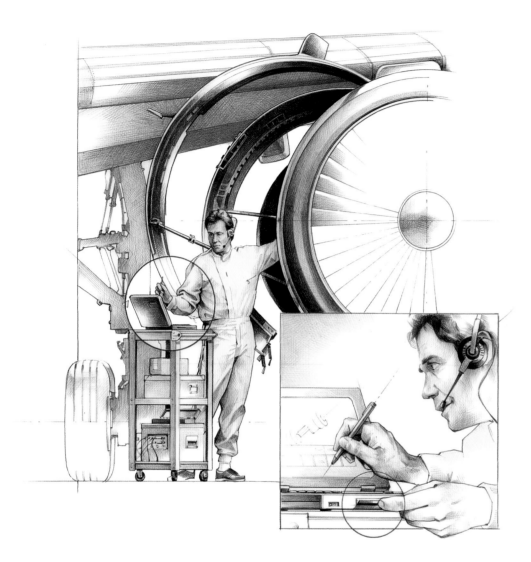

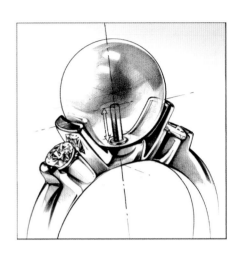

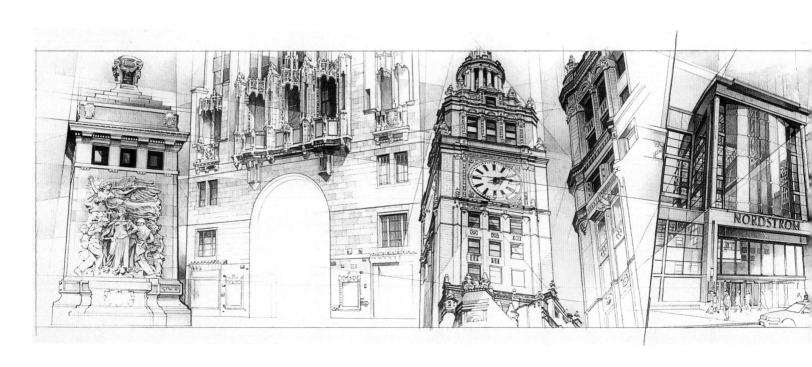

Bruce Morser

Gerald & Cullen Rapp, Inc.
108 East 35 St., New York, NY 10016
Ph: (212) 889-3337 Fax (212) 889-3341
www.theispot.com/artist/morser

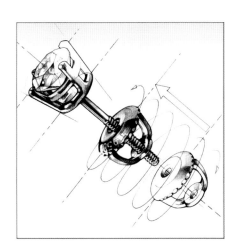

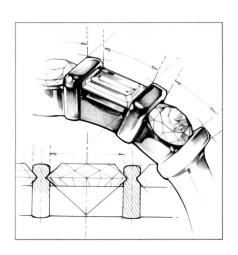

Gerald & Cullen Rapp, Inc.
108 East 35 St., New York, NY 10016
Ph: (212) 889-3337 Fax (212) 889-3341
www.theispot.com/artist/obrien

James O'Brien

Gerald & Cullen Rapp, Inc.
108 East 35 St., New York, NY 10016
Ph: (212) 889-3337 Fax (212) 889-3341
www.theispot.com/artist/obrien

John Pirman

Gerald & Cullen Rapp, Inc.
108 East 35 St., New York, NY 10016
Ph: (212) 889-3337 Fax (212) 889-3341
www.theispot.com/artist/pirman

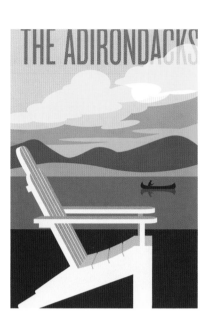

John Pirman

Gerald & Cullen Rapp, Inc.
108 East 35 St., New York, NY 10016
Ph: (212) 889-3337 Fax (212) 889-3341
www.theispot.com/artist/pirman

Jean-Francois Podevin

Gerald & Cullen Rapp, Inc.
108 East 35th St. , New York, NY 10016
Ph: (212) 889-3337 Fax: (212) 889-3341
www.theispot.com/artist/podevin

Jean-Francois Podevin

Gerald & Cullen Rapp, Inc.
108 East 35th St. , New York, NY 10016
Ph: (212) 889-3337 Fax: (212) 889-3341
www.theispot.com/artist/podevin

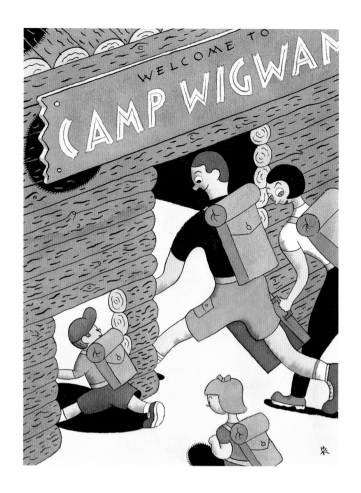

108 East 35th St, New York, NY. 10016   212-889-3337 Fax: 212-889-3341
www.marc-rosenthal.com
www.theispot.com/artist/rosenthal

Alison Seiffer

Gerald & Cullen Rapp, Inc.
108 East 35 St., New York, NY 10016
Ph: (212) 889-3337 Fax (212) 889-3341
www.theispot.com/artist/seiffer

Alison Seiffer

Gerald & Cullen Rapp, Inc.
108 East 35 St., New York, NY 10016
Ph: (212) 889-3337 Fax (212) 889-3341
www.theispot.com/artist/seiffer

Gerald & Cullen Rapp, Inc.
108 East 35 St., New York, NY 10016
Ph: (212) 889-3337 Fax (212) 889-3341
www.theispot.com/artist/seth

Seth

Gerald & Cullen Rapp, Inc.
108 East 35 St., New York, NY 10016
Ph: (212) 889-3337   Fax (212) 889-3341
www.theispot.com/artist/seth

James Steinberg

Gerald & Cullen Rapp, Inc.
108 East 35 St., New York, NY 10016
Ph: (212) 889-3337 Fax (212) 889-3341
www.theispot.com/artist/steinberg

James Steinberg

Gerald & Cullen Rapp, Inc.
108 East 35 St., New York, NY 10016
Ph: (212) 889-3337 Fax (212) 889-3341
www.theispot.com/artist/steinberg

DREW STRUZAN
www.drewstruzan.com

represented by
GERALD & CULLEN RAPP
2 1 2 . 8 8 9 . 3 3 3 7

CREATURE FROM THE BLACK LAGOON

Elizabeth Traynor

Gerald & Cullen Rapp, Inc.
108 East 35 St., New York, NY 10016
Ph: (212) 889-3337 Fax (212) 889-3341
www.theispot.com/artist/traynor

1,000 MEXICAN *Recipes*

BY MARGE POORE

POWER

THE CONGRESSIONAL COLLECTION
1966 of 2000
WILLIAM V. ROTH, Jr.
Historical Society of Delaware

Elizabeth Traynor

Gerald & Cullen Rapp, Inc.
108 East 35 St., New York, NY 10016
Ph: (212) 889-3337 Fax (212) 889-3341
www.theispot.com/artist/traynor

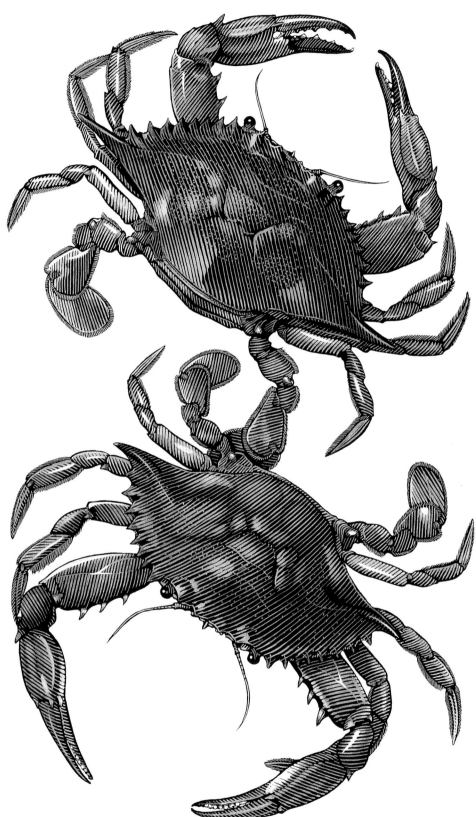

anders wenngren

gerald & cullen rapp, inc.
108 east 35 st., new york, ny 10016
ph: 212 889-3337   fax: 212 889-3341
www.theispot.com/artist/awenngren

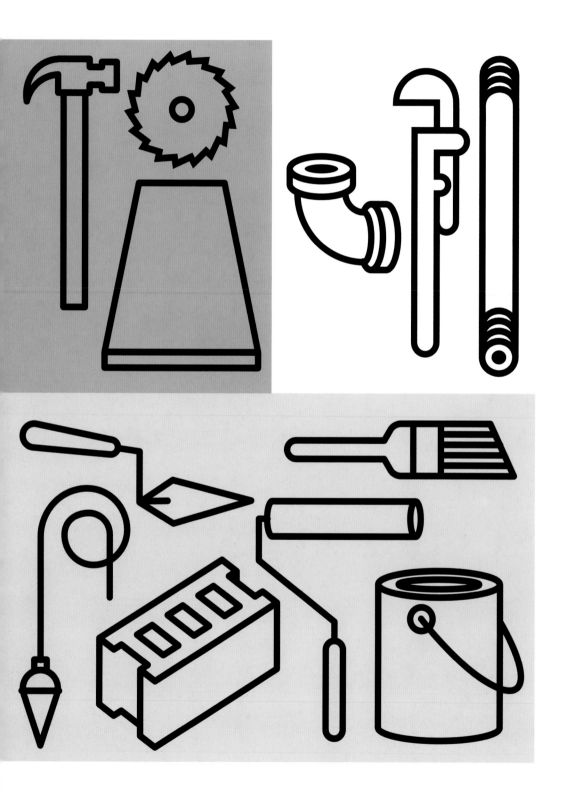

146

anders wenngren
gerald & cullen rapp, inc.
108 east 35 st., new york, ny 10016
ph: 212 889-3337 fax: 212 889-3341
www.theispot.com/artist/awenngren

Michael Witte

Gerald & Cullen Rapp, Inc.
108 East 35 St., New York, NY 10016
Ph. (212) 889-3337 Fax (212) 889-3341
www.theispot.com/artist/witte

Michael Witte

Gerald & Cullen Rapp, Inc.
108 East 35 St., New York, NY 10016
Ph: (212) 889-3337 Fax (212) 889-3341
www.theispot.com/artist/witte

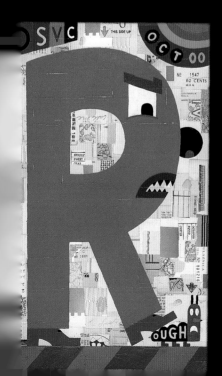

BRAD YEO

GERALD & CULLEN RAPP, INC. 108 EAST 35 ST., NEW YORK, NY 10016
PH: (212) 889-3337 FAX: (212) 889-3341 WWW.THEISPOT.COM/ARTIST/YEO

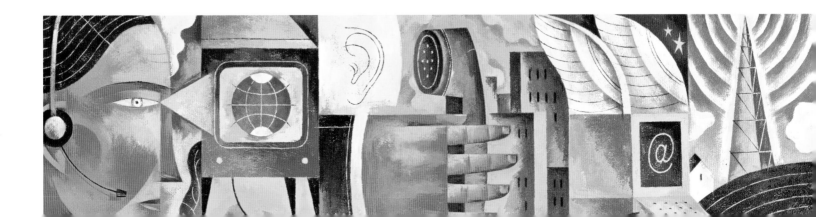

CONRAD REPRESENTS

www.conradreps.com

2149 LYON ST #5 SAN FRANCISCO, CA 94115 / T 415.921.7140 F 415.921.3939 E art@conradreps.com W conradreps.com

Rafael Lopez

2149 LYON ST #5 SAN FRANCISCO, CA 94115 / T 415.921.7140 F 415.921.3939 E art@conradreps.com W conradreps.com

CONRAD REPRESENTS

Rafael Lopez

CONRAD REPRESENTS

2149 LYON ST #5   SAN FRANCISCO, CA 94115 / T 415.921.7140   F 415.921.3939   E art@conradreps.com   W conradreps.com

Ron Tanovitz

2149 LYON ST #5 SAN FRANCISCO, CA 94115 / T 415.921.7140 F 415.921.3939 E art@conradreps.com W conradreps.com | CONRAD REPRESENTS

Eve Steccati

2149 LYON ST #5 SAN FRANCISCO, CA 94115 / T 415.921.7140 F 415.921.3939 E art@conradreps.com W conradreps.com | CONRAD REPRESENTS

Eric Westbrook

CONRAD REPRESENTS

2149 LYON ST #5   SAN FRANCISCO, CA 94115 / T 415.921.7140   F 415.921.3939   E art@conradreps.com   W conradreps.com

Neal Aspinall

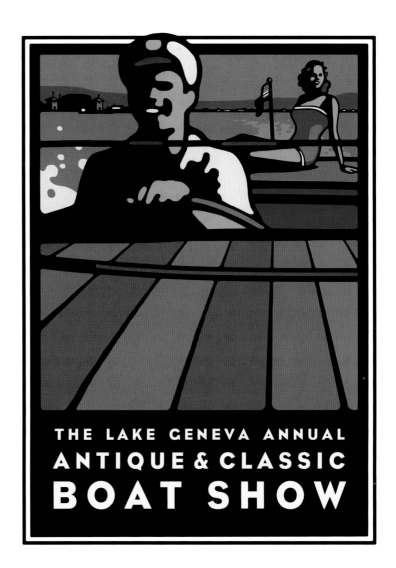

CONRAD REPRESENTS

2149 LYON ST #5 SAN FRANCISCO, CA 94115 / T 415.921.7140 F 415.921.3939 E art@conradreps.com W conradreps.com

Max Seabaugh

CONRAD REPRESENTS

2149 LYON ST #5 SAN FRANCISCO, CA 94115 / T 415.921.7140 F 415.921.3939 E art@conradreps.com W conradreps.com

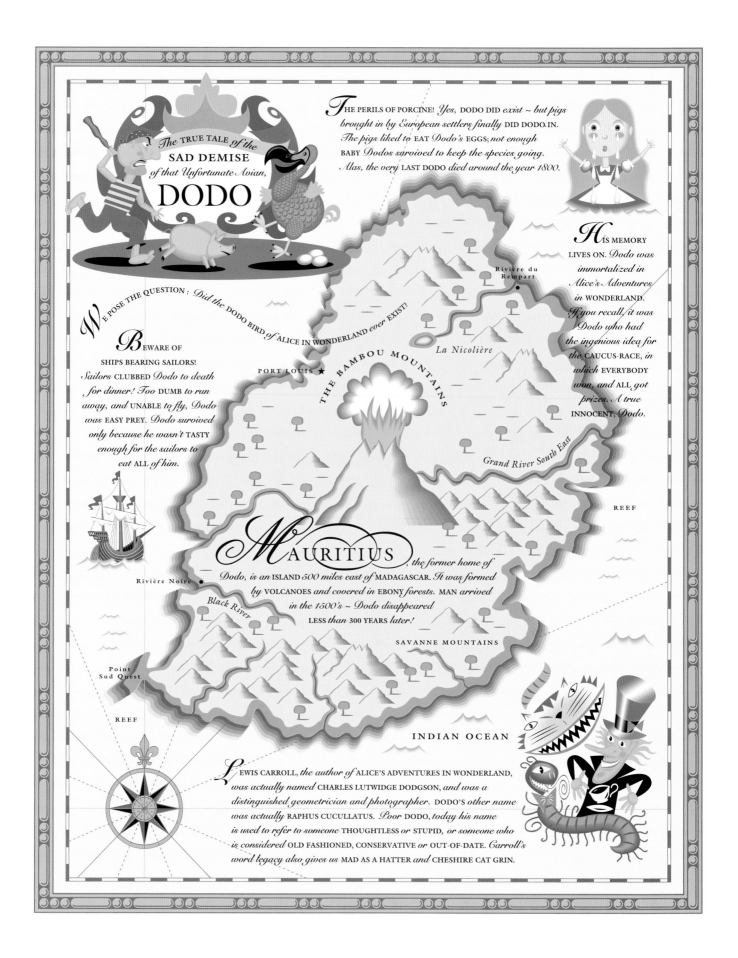

The TRUE TALE of the SAD DEMISE of that Unfortunate Avian, DODO

THE PERILS OF PORCINE! Yes, DODO DID exist ~ but pigs brought in by European settlers finally DID DODO. IN. The pigs liked to EAT Dodo's EGGS; not enough BABY Dodos survived to keep the species going. Alas, the very LAST DODO died around the year 1800.

WE POSE THE QUESTION : Did the DODO BIRD of ALICE IN WONDERLAND ever EXIST?

BEWARE OF SHIPS BEARING SAILORS! Sailors CLUBBED Dodo to death for dinner! Too DUMB to run away, and UNABLE to fly, Dodo was EASY PREY. Dodo survived only because he wasn't TASTY enough for the sailors to eat ALL of him.

HIS MEMORY LIVES ON. Dodo was immortalized in Alice's Adventures in WONDERLAND. If you recall, it was Dodo who had the ingenious idea for the CAUCUS-RACE, in which EVERYBODY won, and ALL got prizes. A true INNOCENT, Dodo.

Rivière du Rempart

La Nicolière

PORT LOUIS ★

THE BAMBOU MOUNTAINS

Grand River South East

REEF

MAURITIUS, the former home of Dodo, is an ISLAND 500 miles east of MADAGASCAR. It was formed by VOLCANOES and covered in EBONY forests. MAN arrived in the 1500's ~ Dodo disappeared LESS than 300 YEARS later!

Rivière Noire

Black River

SAVANNE MOUNTAINS

Point Sud Ouest

REEF

INDIAN OCEAN

LEWIS CARROLL, the author of ALICE'S ADVENTURES IN WONDERLAND, was actually named CHARLES LUTWIDGE DODGSON, and was a distinguished geometrician and photographer. DODO'S other name was actually RAPHUS CUCULLATUS. Poor DODO, today his name is used to refer to someone THOUGHTLESS or STUPID, or someone who is considered OLD FASHIONED, CONSERVATIVE or OUT-OF-DATE. Carroll's word legacy also gives us MAD AS A HATTER and CHESHIRE CAT GRIN.

Charles Bell

CONRAD REPRESENTS

2149 LYON ST #5 SAN FRANCISCO, CA 94115 / T 415.921.7140 F 415.921.3939 E art@conradreps.com W conradreps.com

Daniel Renner

2149 LYON ST #5   SAN FRANCISCO, CA 94115 / T 415.921.7140   F 415.921.3939   E art@conradreps.com   W conradreps.com

CONRAD REPRESENTS

Chris Buzelli

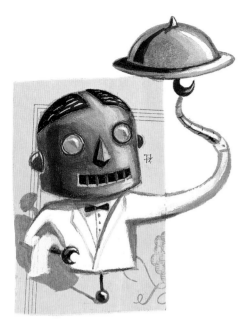

CONRAD REPRESENTS

2149 LYON ST #5 SAN FRANCISCO, CA 94115 / T 415.921.7140 F 415.921.3939 E art@conradreps.com W conradreps.com

Steve Morris

Dave Stevenson

2149 LYON ST #5 SAN FRANCISCO, CA 94115 / T 415.921.7140 F 415.921.3939 E art@conradreps.com W conradreps.com CONRAD REPRESENTS

Leland Klanderman

CONRAD REPRESENTS

2149 LYON ST #5 SAN FRANCISCO, CA 94115 / T 415.921.7140 F 415.921.3939 E art@conradreps.com W conradreps.com

Michael Gibbs

CONRAD REPRESENTS

2149 LYON ST #5 SAN FRANCISCO, CA 94115 / T 415.921.7140 F 415.921.3939 E art@conradreps.com W conradreps.com

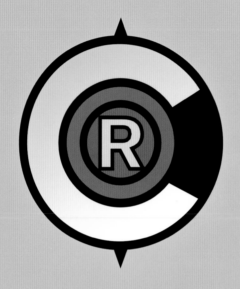

CONRAD REPRESENTS

---

www.conradreps.com

2149 LYON ST #5 SAN FRANCISCO, CA 94115 / T 415.921.7140 F 415.921.3939 E art@conradreps.com W conradreps.com

Lori Nowicki
& Associates

212:243:5888 | lori@lorinowicki.com
fax: 212:243:5955 | www.lorinowicki.com

Antonello Silverini

rep: **Lori Nowicki**
& Associates
212:243:5888 | lori@lorinowicki.com
fax: 212:243:5955 | www.lorinowicki.com

Stacy Peterson

rep: **Lori Nowicki**
& Associates
212:243:5888 | lori@lorinowicki.com
fax: 212:243:5955 | www.lorinowicki.com

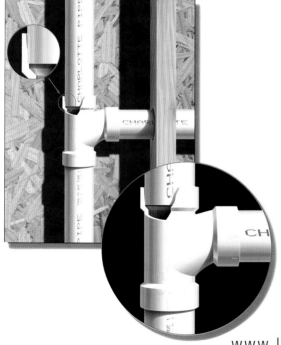

Cecilia Waxberg

rep: **Lori Nowicki**
& Associates
212:243:5888 | lori@lorinowicki.com
fax: 212:243:5955 | www.lorinowicki.com

$$v_{L1} = v_{l1} \frac{L_1}{100l_1} = A \frac{L_1^2}{100l_1} + B \frac{L_1}{100l_1}, \text{ etc.}$$

$$v_{L1} = v_{l1} \frac{L_1}{100l_1} = A \frac{L_1^2}{100l_1} + B \frac{L_1}{100l_1}, \text{ etc.}$$

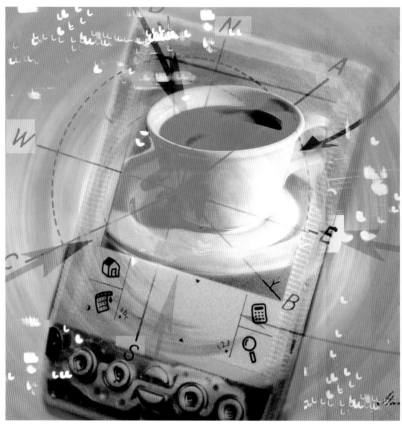

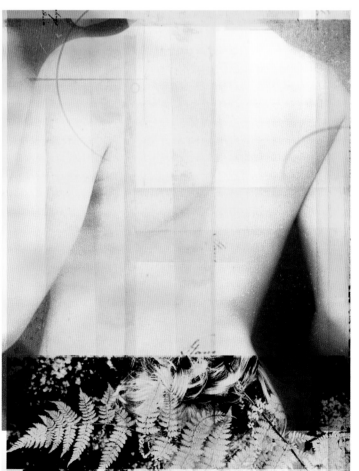

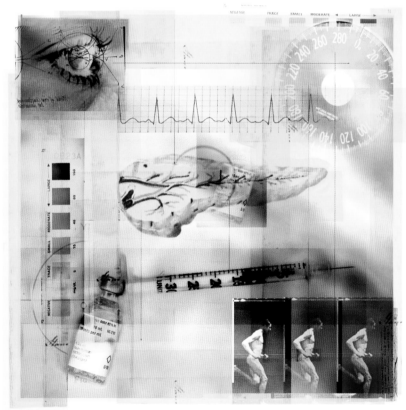

rep: **Lori Nowicki**
& Associates
212:243:5888 | lori@lorinowicki.com
fax: 212:243:5955
www.lorinowicki.com

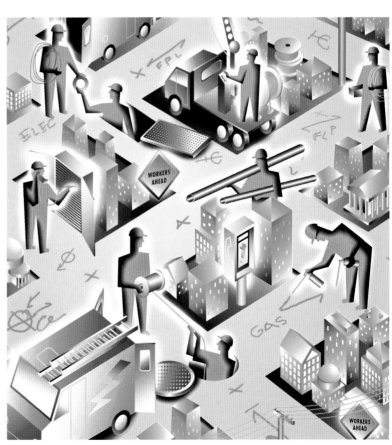

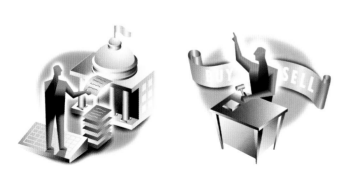

rep: **Lori Nowicki**
& Associates

www.lorinowicki.com | lori@lorinowicki.com
fax: 212:243:5955 | 212:243:5888

RICHARD

SOLOMON

305 EAST 50TH STREET • SUITE 1 • NEW YORK, NEW YORK 10022

PAUL COX • JOHN DAWSON • JOHN COLLIER • DONATO GIANCOLA • GREGORY MANCHESS • BILL NELSON • LOREN LONG • ANDREA VENTURA • C. F. PAYNE • JAMES BENNETT • MARK SUMMERS • RAYMOND VERDAGUER • MURRAY KIMBER • DOUGLAS SMITH • DAVID JOHNSON • KENT BARTON • GARY KELLEY • STEPHEN JOHNSON

TEL 212.223.9545 FAX 212.223.9633 WWW.RICHARDSOLOMON.COM

HEAR NO EVIL, SEE NO EVIL, SPEAK NO EVIL/SCRATCHBOARD

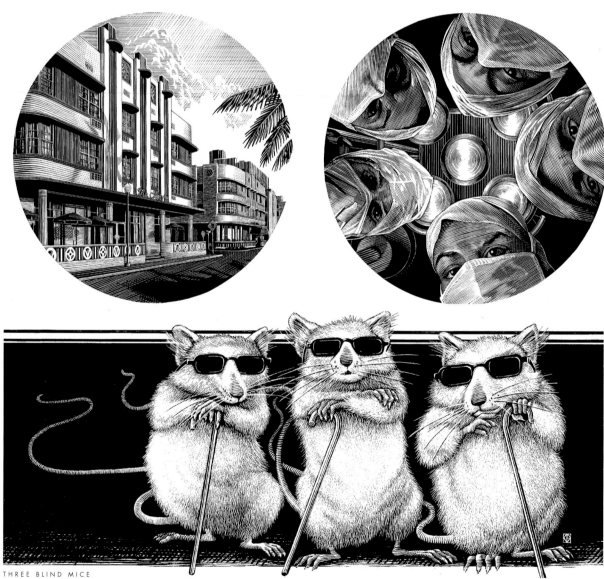

THREE BLIND MICE

IN HIS ANGER MOSES BREAKS THE TABLETS/SCRATCHBOARD

SICK WORLD/OIL

THE WILLIAMS SISTERS

EMINEM

EL PRESIDENTE

KERMIT'S LOUNGE/OIL

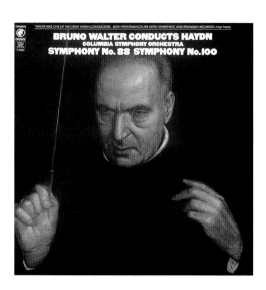

THE LAST ASSET BY EDITH WHARTON/PASTEL & GOUACHE

RICHARD SOLOMON
305 E 50TH ST • NYC 10022
ARTISTS REPRESENTATIVE

212.223.9545 FAX: 212.223.9633

WEBSITE: WWW.RICHARDSOLOMON.COM

SWIMMER ABOVE THE LAKE/OIL

BOYS TO GENTLEMEN/WATERCOLOR

FIRST DATE: DO'S AND DON'TS

THE UPPER EAST SIDE

THE LEOPARD BY GIUSEPPE TOMASI DI LAMPEDUSA/WATERCOLOR

RICHARD SOLOMON
ARTISTS REPRESENTATIVE

305 E 50TH ST • NYC 10022

212.223.9545 FAX: 212.223.9633

WEBSITE: WWW.RICHARDSOLOMON.COM

TIDAL POOLS/ACRYLIC

COUGARS: A MOST AMUSING AMBUSH

GRAY WOLVES: TAKING A BREAK/ACRYLIC

THE FAR REACH OF HUMANITY: MINING THE SATELLITES OF OUR SOLAR SYSTEM / OIL

RICHARD SOLOMON
305 E 50TH ST · NYC 10022
ARTISTS REPRESENTATIVE

212.223.9545 FAX: 212.223.9633 WEBSITE: WWW.RICHARDSOLOMON.COM

DONATO GIANCOLA IS AVAILABLE FOR LARGE-SCALE SPATIAL ENVIRONMENTS: CUSTOM PANORAMA PROJECTS, DIORAMAS, MURALS, AND TROMPE L'OEIL, IN BOTH PAINTED AND DIGITIZED VERSIONS.

RICHARD SOLOMON
305 E 50TH ST ▪ NYC 10022
ARTISTS REPRESENTATIVE

212.223.9545 FAX: 212.223.9633

WEBSITE: WWW.RICHARDSOLOMON.COM

THE OLD CURIOSITY SHOP BY CHARLES DICKENS/PEN & INK

RICHARD SOLOMON
305 E 50TH ST • NYC 10022
ARTISTS REPRESENTATIVE

212.223.9545 FAX: 212.223.9633   WEBSITE: WWW.RICHARDSOLOMON.COM

BOB DYLAN: SUBTERRANEAN HOMESICK BLUES/INK & WATERCOLOR

RICHARD SOLOMON
ARTISTS REPRESENTATIVE
305 E 50TH ST • NYC 10022

212.223.9545 FAX: 212.223.9633

WEBSITE: WWW.RICHARDSOLOMON.COM

A CULTURE OF POETS/PASTEL

CADILLAC PROTOTYPE CONCEPT

MCGWIRE: THE SUMMER OF 70

RICHARD SOLOMON
305 E 50TH ST • NYC 10022
ARTISTS REPRESENTATIVE

212.223.9545 FAX: 212.223.9633   WEBSITE: WWW.RICHARDSOLOMON.COM

TIGHTROPE TANGO/PASTEL

RICHARD SOLOMON
305 E 50TH ST • NYC 10022
ARTISTS REPRESENTATIVE

212.223.9545 FAX: 212.223.9633 | WEBSITE: WWW.RICHARDSOLOMON.COM

SMOOTH SAILING/ OIL

MEET DRINK AND BE MERRY

WHEN IRISH EYES ARE SMILING

HIGHWAYS IN THE SKY/OIL

FROM BARCELONA WITH LOVE

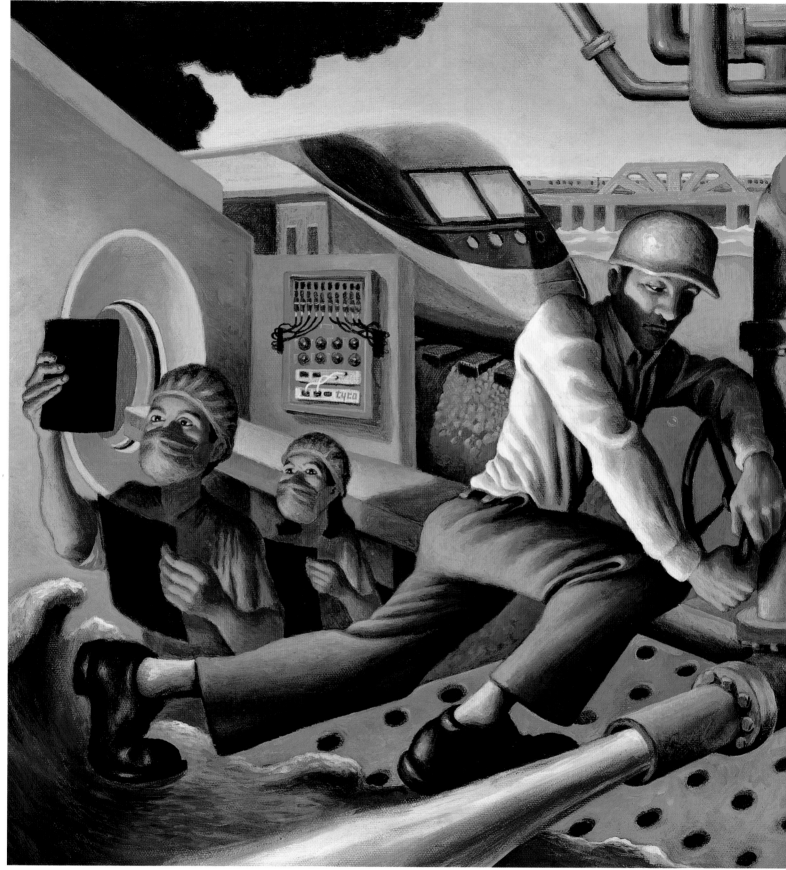

THE TYCO CORPORATION: LEADING THE WORLD IN MANUFACTURING: TELECOMMUNICATIONS, ELECTRONICS, WATER CONTROL, AND MEDICAL PRODUCTS/ACRYL

LOREN LONG IS AVAILABLE FOR LARGE-SCALE SPATIAL ENVIRONMENTS: CUSTOM PANORAMA PROJECTS, DIORAMAS, MURALS, AND TROMPE L'OEIL, IN BOTH PAINTED AND DIGITIZED VERSIONS.

NIGHT CROSSING/OIL

ELLINGTON

A LABOR OF LOVE

RICHARD SOLOMON
305 E 50TH ST • NYC 10022
ARTISTS REPRESENTATIVE

212.223.9545 FAX: 212.223.9633

WEBSITE: WWW.RICHARDSOLOMON.COM

THE "NEW" OLD ECONOMY/OIL

RICHARD SOLOMON
305 E 50TH ST • NYC 10022
ARTISTS REPRESENTATIVE

212.223.9545 FAX: 212.223.9633 | WEBSITE: WWW.RICHARDSOLOMON.COM

NICHOLSON/COLORED PENCIL

MADONNA

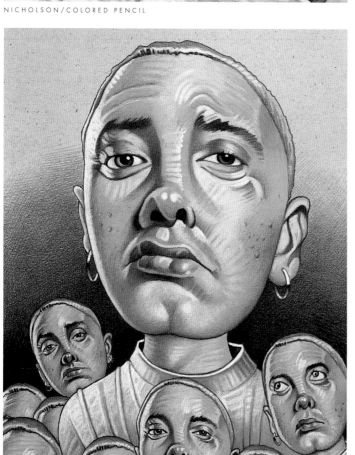

EMINEM

STALLONE

212.223.9545 FAX: 212.223.9633

RICHARD SOLOMON
305 E 50TH ST • NYC 10022
ARTISTS REPRESENTATIVE

WEBSITE: WWW.RICHARDSOLOMON.COM

THE PRODUCERS/COLORED PENCIL

THE REMARKABLE FARKLE MCBRIDE BY JOHN LITHGOW/MIXED MEDIA

RICHARD SOLOMON
305 E 50TH ST • NYC 10022
ARTISTS REPRESENTATIVE

212.223.9545 FAX: 212.223.9633

WEBSITE: WWW.RICHARDSOLOMON.COM

SOCIETY OF ILLUSTRATORS CALL FOR ENTRIES/MIXED MEDIA

CASEY AT THE BAT

DREYER'S ICE CREAM: CHOCOLATE ALMOND BAR

RICHARD SOLOMON
305 E 50TH ST • NYC 10022
ARTISTS REPRESENTATIVE

212.223.9545 FAX: 212.223.9633

WEBSITE: WWW.RICHARDSOLOMON.COM

207

IN THE ARCADE, 1904 / SCRATCHBOARD & WATERCOLOR

HORNBLOWER AND THE ATROPOS BY C.S. FORESTER/SCRATCHBOARD & WATERCOLOR

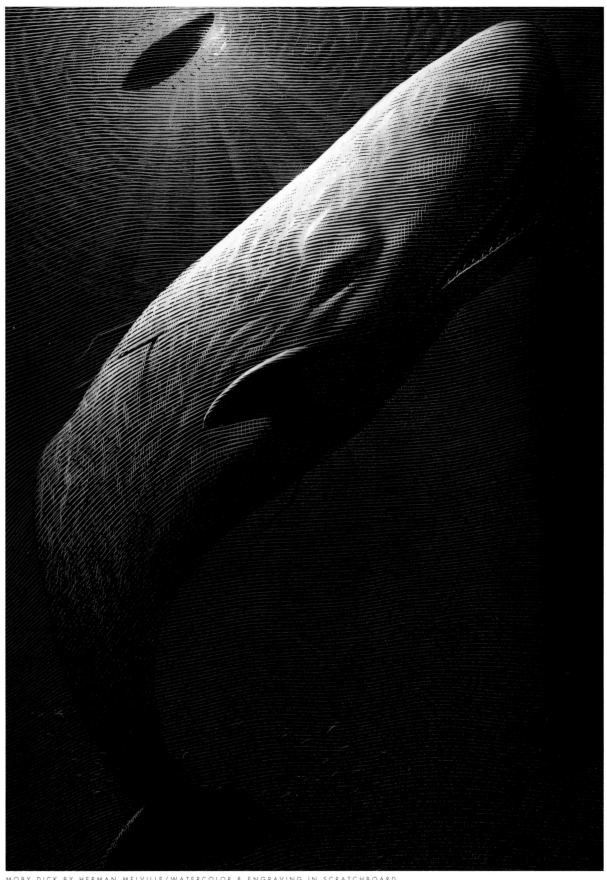

MOBY DICK BY HERMAN MELVILLE / WATERCOLOR & ENGRAVING IN SCRATCHBOARD

RICHARD SOLOMON
305 E 50TH ST • NYC 10022
ARTISTS REPRESENTATIVE

212.223.9545 FAX: 212.223.9633   WEBSITE: WWW.RICHARDSOLOMON.COM

SERENA WILLIAMS/WATERCOLOR & ENGRAVING IN SCRATCHBOARD

ANDREA VENTURA

JOLTIN' JOE DIMAGGIO / MIXED MEDIA

CAT ON A HOT TIN ROOF/MIXED MEDIA

RICHARD SOLOMON
ARTISTS REPRESENTATIVE

212.223.9545 FAX: 212.223.9633   305 E 50TH ST • NYC 10022   WEBSITE: WWW.RICHARDSOLOMON.COM

1.888.277.7200

i2i

www.i2iart.com

DANIEL CHEN	KEVIN GHIGLIONE	ANSON LIAW
TRACY WALKER	ALANNA CAVANAGH	TIM ZELTNER
THOM SEVALRUD	CHUM MCLEOD	DOUG MARTIN
ERIK MOHR	IAN PHILLIPS	LAURIE LAFRANCE
HARVEY CHAN	PHILIPPE BÉHA	GREG STEVENSON
HELEN D'SOUZA		GLENN RYAN

e-mail: info@i2iart.com   telephone: 416.505.9522

DANIEL CHEN

Represented by i2i Art Inc.   www.i2iart.com   1.888.277.7200   info@i2iart.com   416.505.9522

TRACY WALKER

TRACY WALKER

THOM SEVALRUD

SUMMER 1985

ErIK mOHr

harvey chan

harvey chan

HELEN D'SOUZA

KEVIN GHIGLIONE

Represented by i2i Art Inc.   www.i2iart.com   1.888.277.7200   info@i2iart.com   416.505.9522

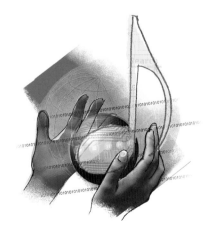

kevin ghiglione

Represented by i2i Art Inc.   www.i2iart.com   1.888.277.7200   info@i2iart.com   416.505.9522

ALANNA CAVANAGH

chum mcleod

Represented by i2i Art Inc.   www.i2iart.com   1.888.277.7200   info@i2iart.com   416.505.9522

ian PHILLIPS

Represented by i2i Art Inc.   www.i2iart.com   1.888.277.7200   info@i2iart.com   416.505.9522

ian PHILLIPS

PHILIPPE BÉHa

Represented by i2i Art Inc.   www.i2iart.com   1.888.277.7200   info@i2iart.com   416.505.9522

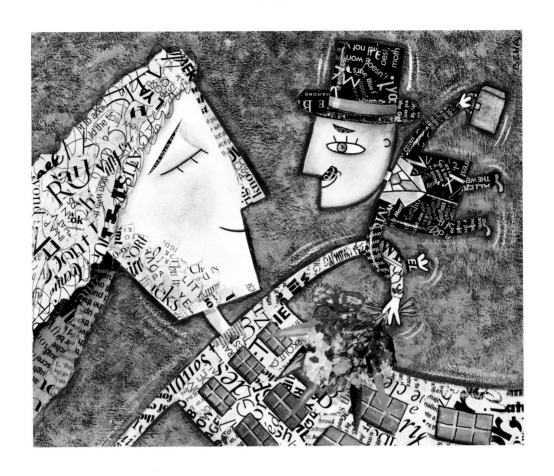

PHILIPPE BÉHa

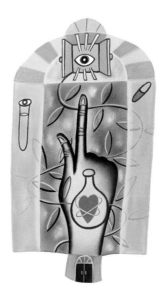

anson liaw

anson liaw

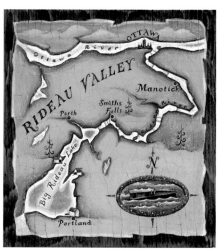

TIM ZELTNER

DOUG MARTIN

DOUG MARTIN

Laurie Lafrance

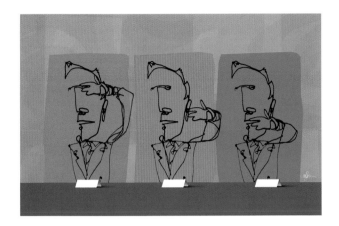

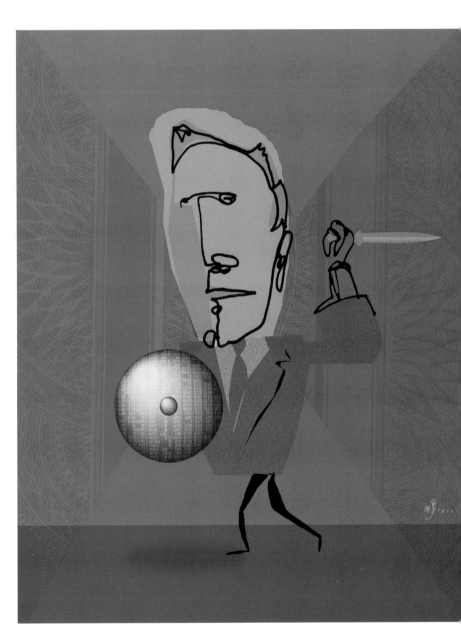

GREG STEVENSON

Glenn Ryan

GLENN RYAN

Represented by i2i Art Inc.   www.i2iart.com   1.888.277.7200   info@i2iart.com   416.505.9522

FASOLINO

CAPLANIS

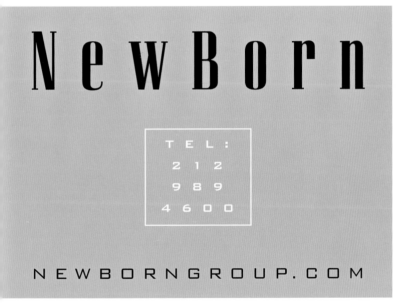

MARSH

GOLDSTROM

JUHASZ

GUTIERREZ

ZACHAROW

GIUSTI

HOWARD

HESS

MCLEAN

ROBERT GIUSTI

TOP: UNITED NATIONS POSTAL ADMINISTRATION   MIDDLE LEFT: OPRAH MAGAZINE   MIDDLE RIGHT: DER SPIEGEL   BOTTOM: PENTAGRAM DESIGN

WILSON MCLEAN

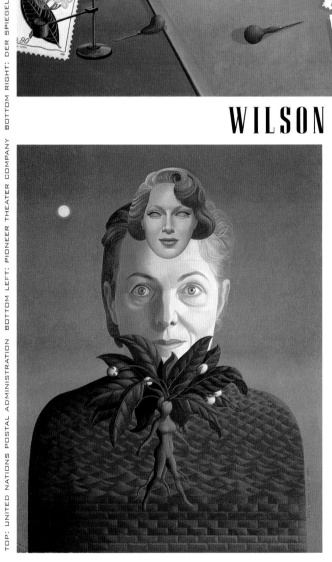

MIKE CAPLANIS

JOHN H HOWARD

The NewBorn Group

Joan Sigman

REPRESENTATIVE

T 212 989 4600   F 212 989 8998

WWW.NEWBORNGROUP.COM

VICTOR JUHASZ

TERESA FASOLINO

The NewBorn Group

Joan Sigman

REPRESENTATIVE

T 212 989 4600   F 212 989 8998

WWW.NEWBORNGROUP.COM

Rubert Sheldrake / Utne Reader

Neil Young / Rolling Stone

Sara Little Turnbull / @issue Magazine

Bertrand Russell / The New York Times Book Review

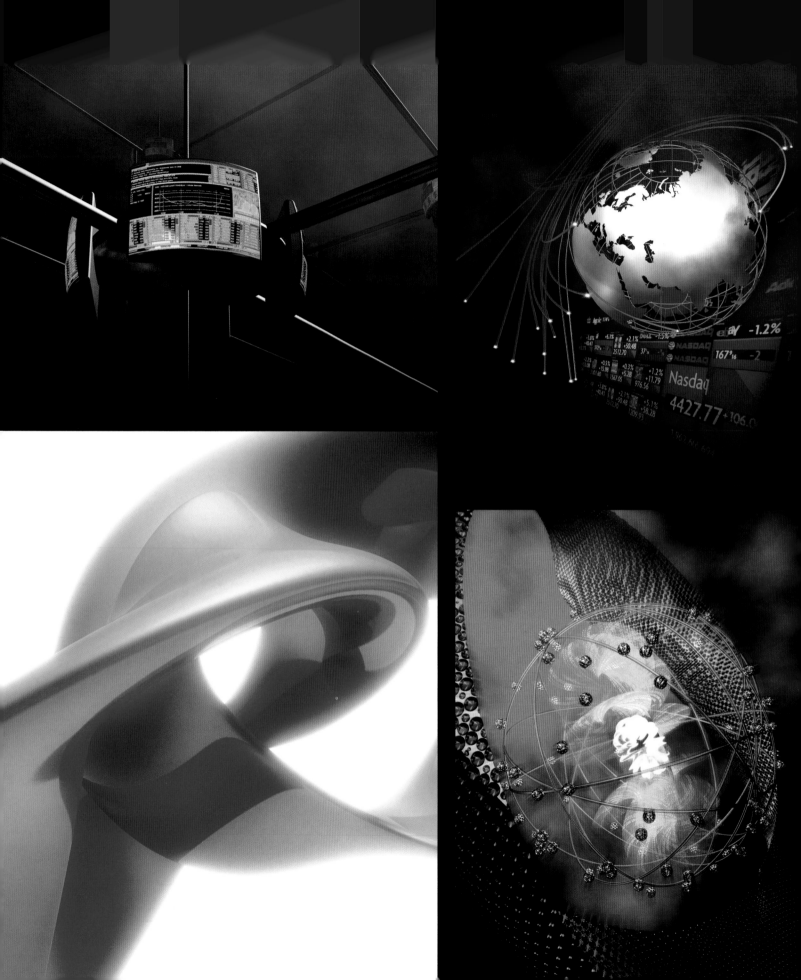

KNOPF

GLIN DIBLEY

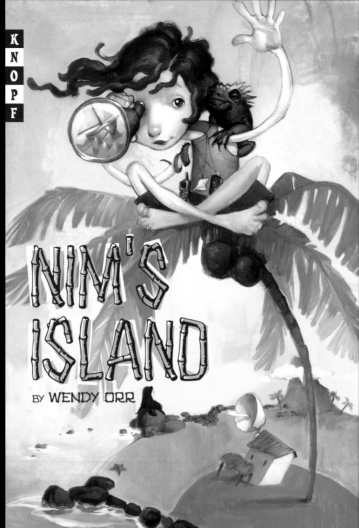

NIM'S ISLAND

BY WENDY ORR

tub-boo-boo

by Margie Palatini
illustrated by Glin Dibley

(S)HANNON

REPRESENTS GLIN DIBLEY

New York   212.333.2551
Los Angeles   323.874.5700
Washington DC   410.349.8669
London   011.44.207.636.1064

Patrick Faricy

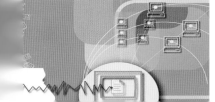

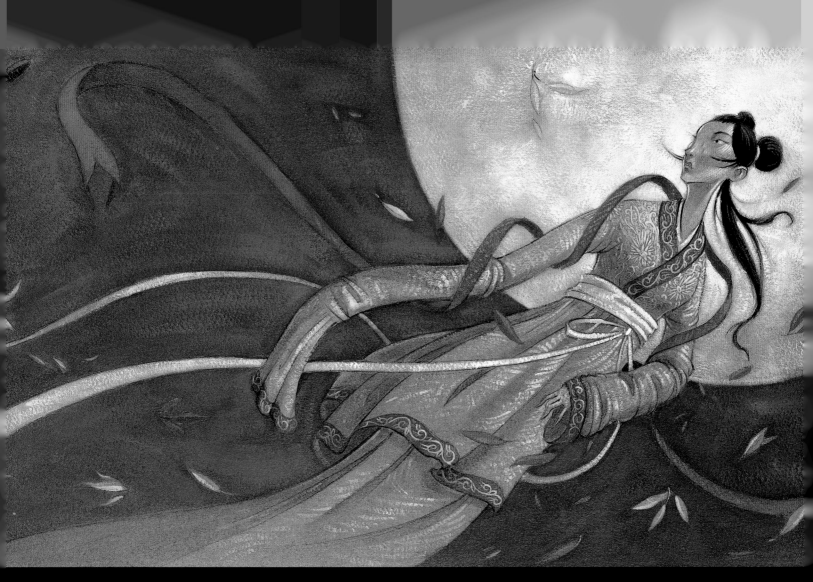

Matthew Herring

www.shannonassociates.com

(S)ha

$ 1000's

KOELSCH
STUDIOS

PROVIDING

THRILLING

and

UNUSUAL

ILLUSTRATIONS

FOR SUCH CLIENTS AS

Land's End

Discovery Channel

Scholastic

Pepsi

Criterion

Corn Nuts

USA Networks

Terminix

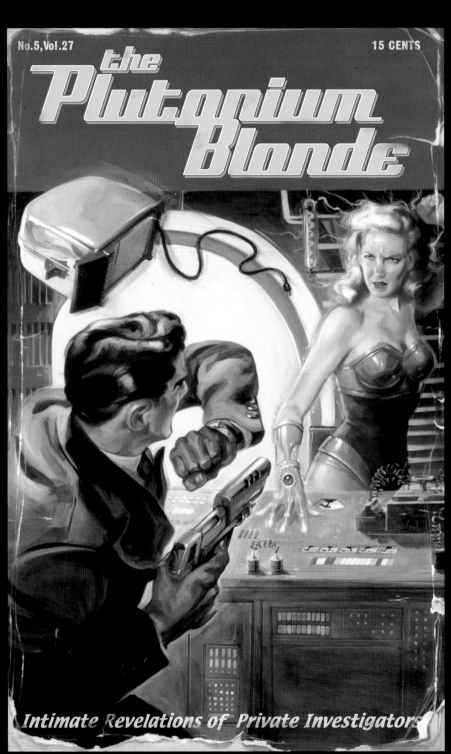

No.5, Vol.27   15 CENTS

the Plutonium Blonde

Intimate Revelations of Private Investigators

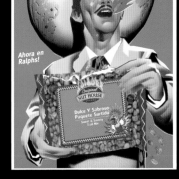

KaGE BAKER

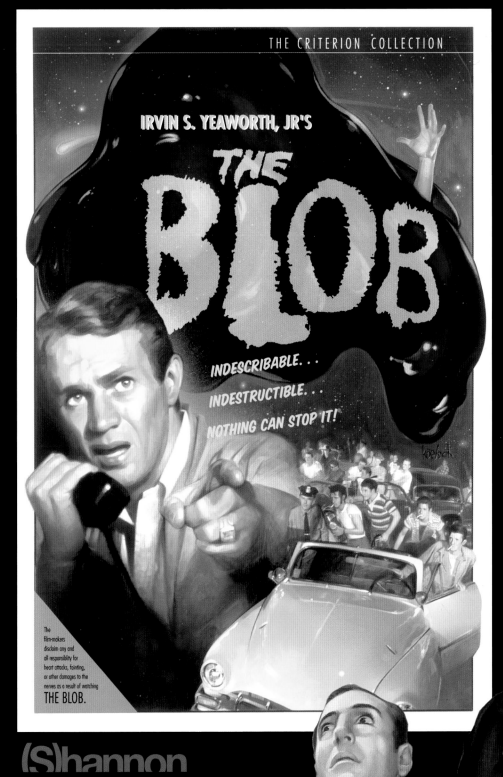

THE CRITERION COLLECTION

IRVIN S. YEAWORTH, JR'S

THE BLOB

INDESCRIBABLE...

INDESTRUCTIBLE...

NOTHING CAN STOP IT!

koelsch

The film-makers disclaim any and all responsibility for heart attacks, fainting, or other damages to the nerves as a result of watching THE BLOB.

KEEN-EYED
ILLUSTRATORS

Match Wits with

CLEVER
ART DIRECTORS

VISIT

KOELSCH STUDIOS

AT

www.SHANNONASSOCIATES.com

(S)hannon

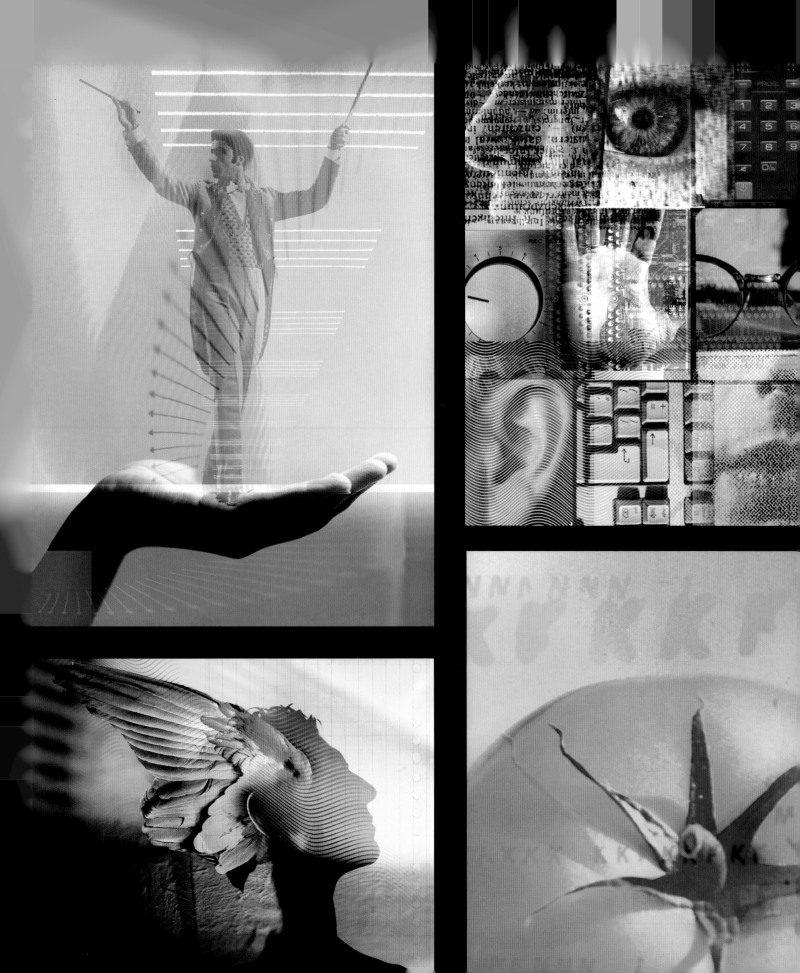

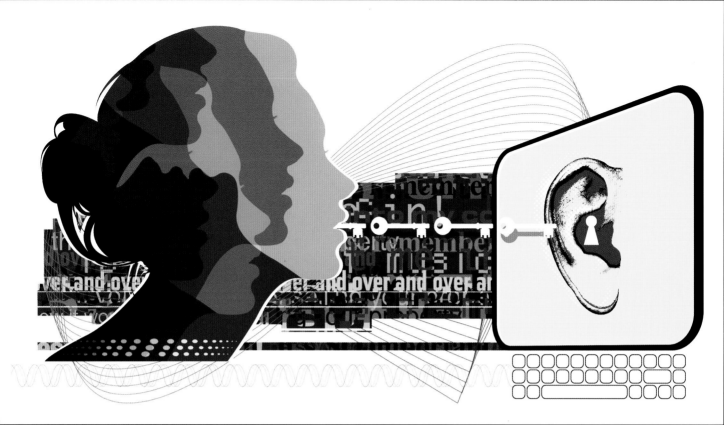

David Newton

J@zz
Jazz at Lincoln Center
www.jazzatlincolncenter.org

THE SECOND ANNUAL
ESSENTIALLY ELLINGTON
BAND DIRECTOR ACADEMY
Wednesday, June 27 to Sunday, July 1, 2001, Snowmass, Colorado

www.jazzaspen.com

Essentially Ellington is made possible with support from: The Jack and Susan Rudin Educational and Scholarship Fund, Danny Kaye and Sylvia Fine Kaye Foundation, Peyel-a Foundation, Surdna Foundation, Verve Music Group, National Endowment for the Arts, Ella Fitzgerald Charitable Foundation, and the Getz Foundation.

Los Angeles   323.874.5700
Washington DC 410.349.8669
London   011.44.207.636.1064

ncent McIndoe

New York   212.333.2551
Los Angeles   323.874.5700
Washington DC   410.349.8669
London   011.44.207.636.106

Yucel.com

Gervasio Gallardo

FRANK & JEFF LAVATY

(212) 427-5632 Fax (212) 427-6372 www.lavatyart.com
e-mail jeff@lavatyart.com Ebba Lavaty, Associate

Representing

STEVEN ADLER

LORI ANZALONE

CRAIG ATTEBERY

JOHN BERKEY

DAVID BIEDRZYCKI

TOM BRENNER

SAL CATALANO

DOM D'ANDREA

DON DEMERS

PAUL DIMARE

CHRIS DUKE

BRUCE EMMETT

TOM FREEMAN

JEFF FITZ-MAURICE

GERVASIO GALLARDO

CORBERT GAUTHIER

JOHN PAUL GENZO

TIM HILDEBRANDT

NEAL HUGHES

GRANT JERDING

DAVID McCALL JOHNSTON

YUAN LEE

ROBERT LOGRIPPO

ROGER LUNDQUIST

DON MANNES

KEVIN MURPHY

CARLOS OCHAGAVIA

RICK REEVES

PETER SCANLAN

DICK SCULLIN

ROBERT SHERRILL

SHANNON STIRNWEISS

BEN VERKAAIK

WERNER WILLIS

ROGER XAVIER

L

FRANK & JEFF LAVATY

(212) 427-5632 Fax (212) 427-6372
www.lavatyart.com e-mail jeff@lavatyart.com
Ebba Lavaty, Associate

Representing

LORI ANZALONE

L
FRANK & JEFF LAVATY
(212) 427-5632 Fax (212) 427-6372
www.lavatyart.com e-mail jeff@lavatyart.com
Ebba Lavaty, Associate

Representing
LORI ANZALONE

L

FRANK & JEFF LAVATY

(212) 427-5632 Fax (212) 427-6372
www.lavatyart.com e-mail jeff@lavatyart.com
Ebba Lavaty, Associate

Representing

CHRIS DUKE

L

FRANK & JEFF LAVATY

(212) 427-5632 Fax (212) 427-6372
www.lavatyart.com e-mail jeff@lavatyart.com
Ebba Lavaty, Associate

Representing

ROBERT SHERRILL

FRANK & JEFF LAVATY

(212) 427-5632 Fax (212) 427-6372
www.lavatyart.com e-mail jeff@lavatyart.com
Ebba Lavaty, Associate

Representing

CORBERT GAUTHIER

L

FRANK & JEFF LAVATY
(212) 427-5632 Fax (212) 427-6372
www.lavatyart.com e-mail jeff@lavatyart.com
Ebba Lavaty, Associate

Representing

YUAN LEE

L

FRANK & JEFF LAVATY

(212) 427-5632 Fax (212) 427-6372
www.lavatyart.com e-mail jeff@lavatyart.com
Ebba Lavaty, Associate

Representing

YUAN LEE

L

FRANK & JEFF LAVATY

(212) 427-5632 Fax (212) 427-6372
www.lavatyart.com e-mail jeff@lavatyart.com
Ebba Lavaty, Associate

Representing

ROBERT LOGRIPPO

L

FRANK & JEFF LAVATY

(212) 427-5632 Fax (212) 427-6372
www.lavatyart.com e-mail jeff@lavatyart.com
Ebba Lavaty, Associate

Representing

DAVID BIEDRZYCKI

L

FRANK & JEFF LAVATY

(212) 427-5632 Fax (212) 427-6372
www.lavatyart.com e-mail jeff@lavatyart.com
Ebba Lavaty, Associate

Representing

TOM FREEMAN

L

FRANK & JEFF LAVATY
(212) 427-5632 Fax (212) 427-6372
www.lavatyart.com e-mail jeff@lavatyart.com
Ebba Lavaty, Associate

Representing

RICK REEVES

L

FRANK & JEFF LAVATY

(212) 427-5632 Fax (212) 427-6372
www.lavatyart.com e-mail jeff@lavatyart.com
Ebba Lavaty, Associate

Representing

DAVID McCALL JOHNSTON

L

FRANK & JEFF LAVATY

(212) 427-5632 Fax (212) 427-6372
www.lavatyart.com e-mail jeff@lavatyart.com
Ebba Lavaty, Associate

Representing

STEVEN ADLER

L

FRANK & JEFF LAVATY

(212) 427-5632 Fax (212) 427-6372
www.lavatyart.com e-mail jeff@lavatyart.com
Ebba Lavaty, Associate

Representing

CRAIG ATTEBERY

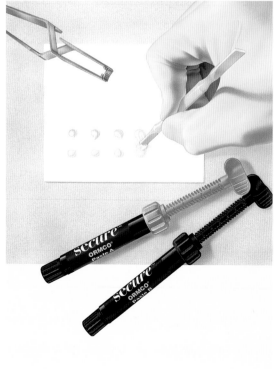

L

FRANK & JEFF LAVATY

(212) 427-5632 Fax (212) 427-6372
www.lavatyart.com e-mail jeff@lavatyart.com
Ebba Lavaty, Associate

Representing

CARLOS OCHAGAVIA

L

FRANK & JEFF LAVATY

(212) 427-5632 Fax (212) 427-6372
www.lavatyart.com e-mail jeff@lavatyart.com
Ebba Lavaty, Associate

Representing

ROGER LUNDQUIST

L

FRANK & JEFF LAVATY

(212) 427-5632 Fax (212) 427-6372
www.lavatyart.com e-mail jeff@lavatyart.com
Ebba Lavaty, Associate

Representing

BEN VERKAAIK

mark HEINE

bruce **GARRITY**

bob KAYGANICH

paine **PROFFITT**

215.232.6666   fax 215.232.6585   www.deborahwolfe.com   **DEBORAH WOLFE LTD**
731 N 24th St., Philadelphia, PA 19130

john SCHREINER

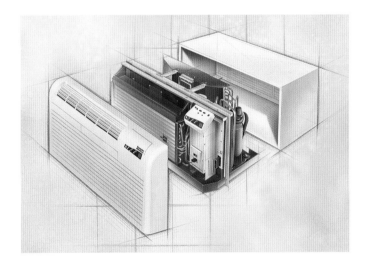

alan KING

jo **TRONC**

215.232.6666   fax 215.232.6585   www.deborahwolfe.com

DEBORAH WOLFE LTD
731 N 24th St., Philadelphia, PA 19130

nancy HARRISON

j.t. MORROW

215.232.6666   fax 215.232.6585   www.deborahwolfe.com

DEBORAH WOLFE LTD
731 N 24th St., Philadelphia, PA 19130

simon SHAW

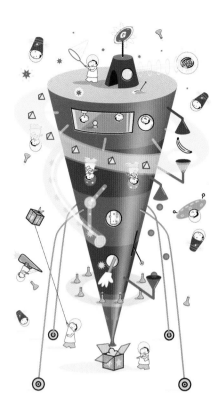

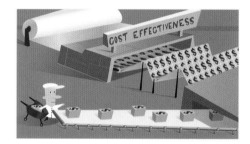

patrick GNAN

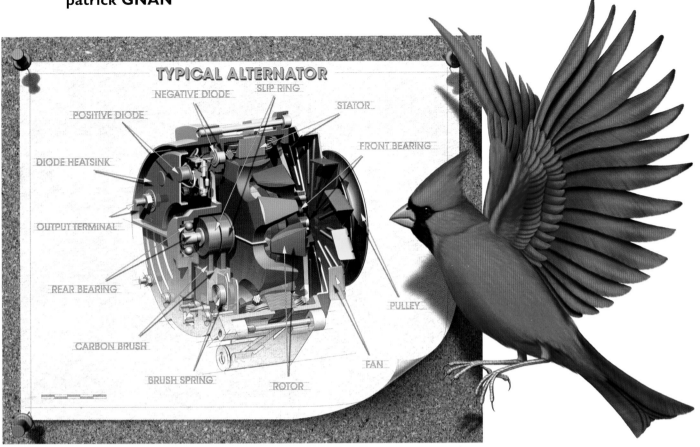

TYPICAL ALTERNATOR

NEGATIVE DIODE
SLIP RING
POSITIVE DIODE
STATOR
DIODE HEATSINK
FRONT BEARING
OUTPUT TERMINAL
REAR BEARING
PULLEY
CARBON BRUSH
FAN
BRUSH SPRING
ROTOR

amy WUMMER

215.232.6666   fax 215.232.6585   www.deborahwolfe.com   **DEBORAH WOLFE LTD**
731 N 24th St., Philadelphia, PA 19130

chris VAN ES

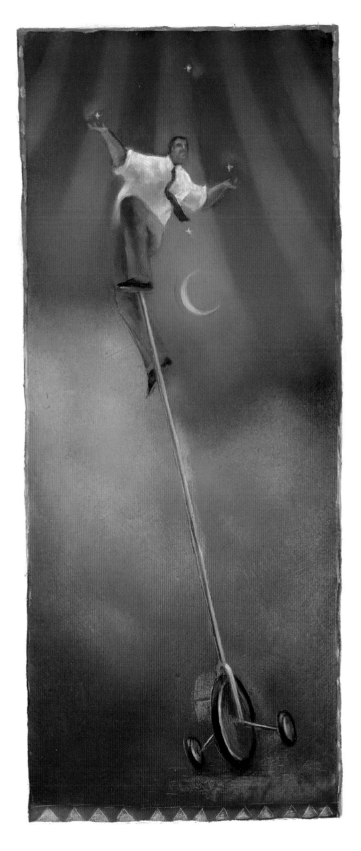

nick **ROTONDO**

dave GARBOT

215.232.6666   fax 215.232.6585   www.deborahwolfe.com

DEBORAH WOLFE LTD
731 N 24th St., Philadelphia, PA 19130

scott FRAY

cindy REVELL

215.232.6666   fax 215.232.6585   www.deborahwolfe.com

DEBORAH WOLFE LTD
731 N 24th St., Philadelphia, PA 19130

jesse **REISCH**

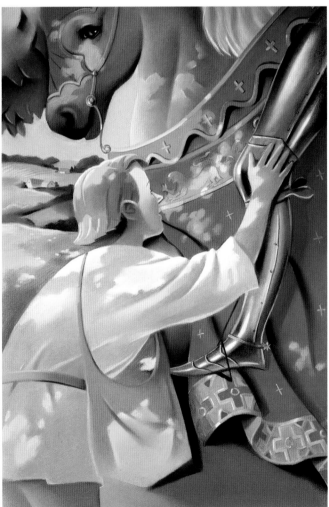

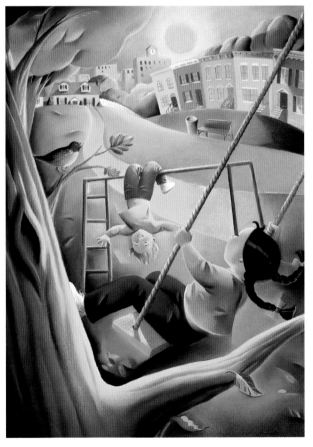

215.232.6666   fax 215.232.6585   www.deborahwolfe.com   **DEBORAH WOLFE LTD**
731 N 24th St., Philadelphia, PA 19130

cam WILSON

215.232.6666   fax 215.232.6585   www.deborahwolfe.com

DEBORAH WOLFE LTD
731 N 24th St., Philadelphia, PA 19130

joel & sharon HARRIS

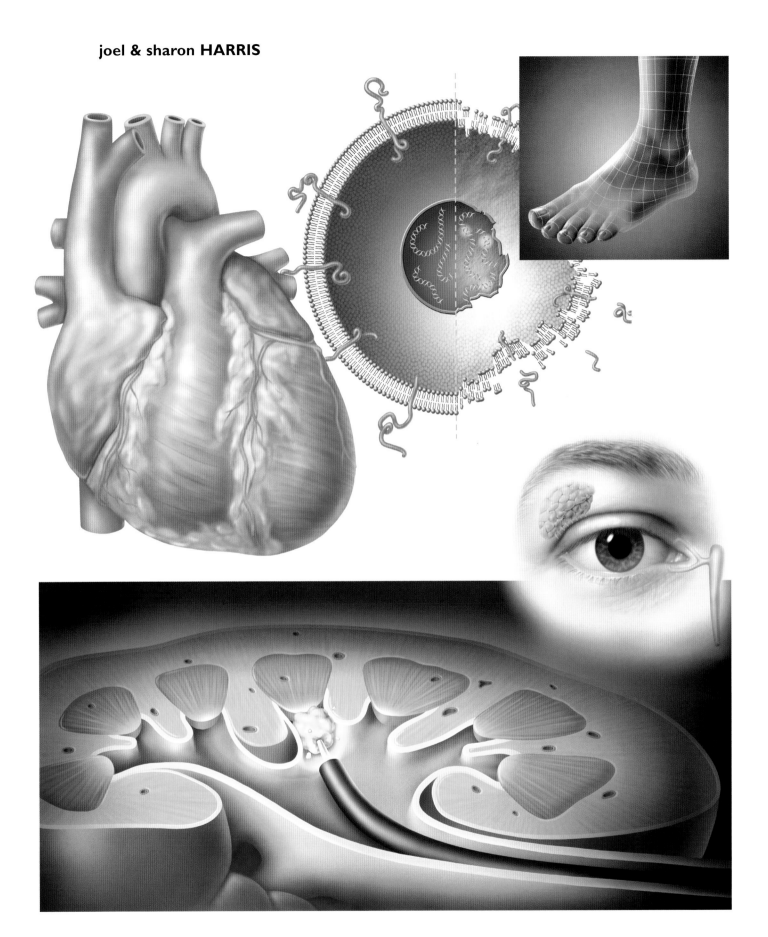

richard HOIT

215.232.6666   fax 215.232.6585   www.deborahwolfe.com

DEBORAH WOLFE LTD
731 N 24th St., Philadelphia, PA 19130

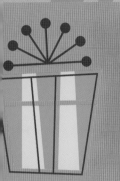

tina healey

represented by
illustration

T 212 749 2220 | E carole.faulkner@illustrationweb.com | W illustrationweb.com : view over 100 unique portfolios

represented by
illustration

T 212 749 2220 | E carole.faulkner@illustrationweb.com| W illustrationweb.com : view over 100 unique portfolios

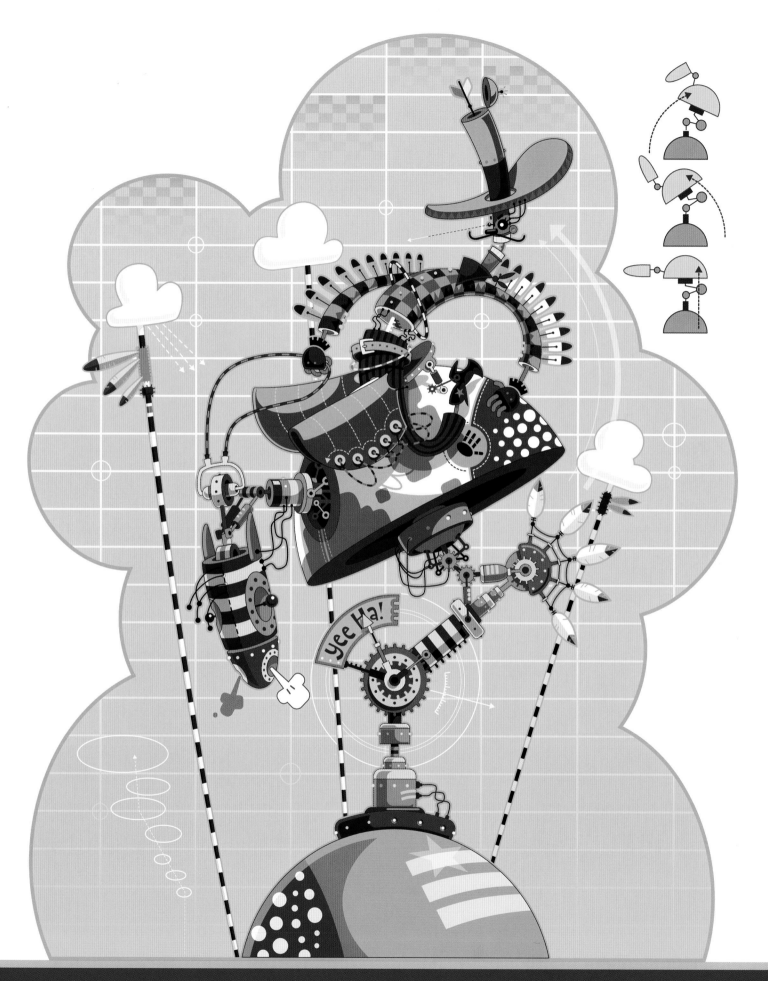

represented by
illustration

T 212 749 2220 | E carole.faulkner@illustrationweb.com | W illustrationweb.com : view over 100 unique portfolios

valerie sinclair

representatives	new york 212.397.7330
patricia lindgren	san francisco 415.788.8552
piper smith	online portfolio at
tricia weber	www.lindgrensmith.com

doug fraser

representatives

patricia lindgren

piper smith

tricia weber

new york 212.397.7330

san francisco 415.788.8552

online portfolio at

www.lindgrensmith.com

doug fraser

representatives
patricia lindgren
piper smith
tricia weber

new york 212.397.7330
san francisco 415.788.8552
online portfolio at
www.lindgrensmith.com

joseph daniel fiedler

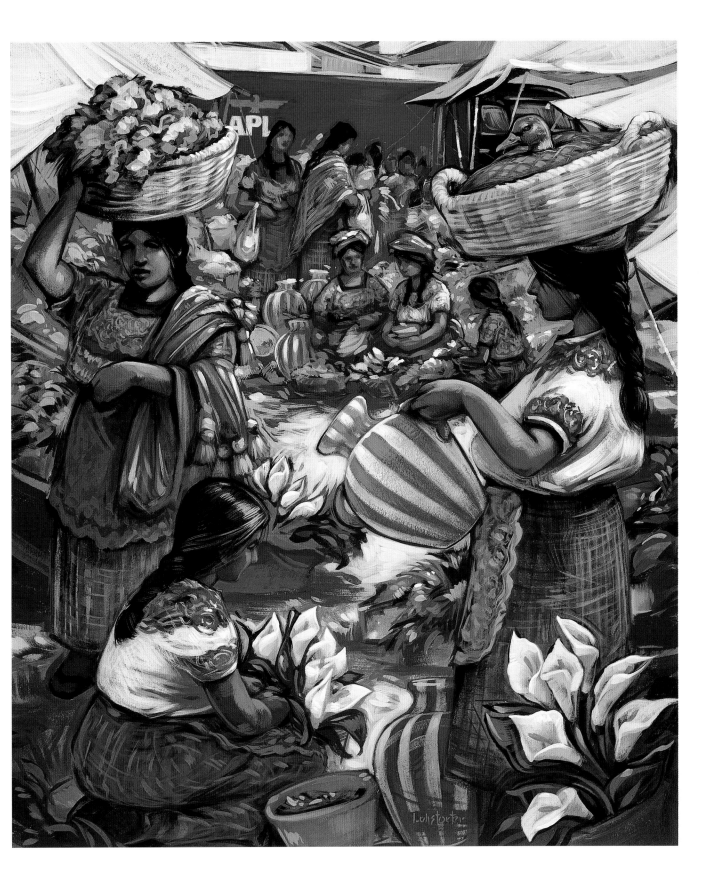

jennifer herbert

representatives
patricia lindgren
piper smith
tricia weber

new york 212.397.7330
san francisco 415.788.8552
online portfolio at
www.lindgrensmith.com

lindgren & smith

steven salerno

representatives
patricia lindgren
piper smith
tricia weber

new york 212.397.7330
san francisco 415.788.8552
online portfolio at
www.lindgrensmith.com

donna racer

representatives	new york 212.397.7330
patricia lindgren	san francisco 415.788.8552
piper smith	online portfolio at
tricia weber	www.lindgrensmith.com

lindgren & smith

robert wagt

representatives
patricia lindgren
piper smith
tricia weber

new york 212.397.7330
san francisco 415.788.8552
online portfolio at
www.lindgrensmith.com

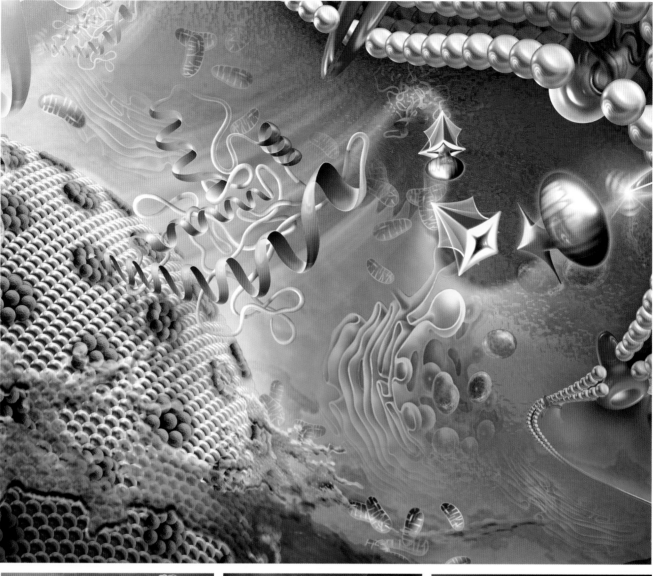
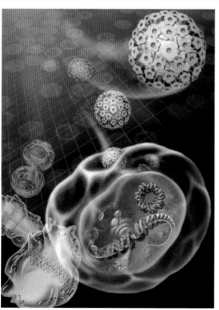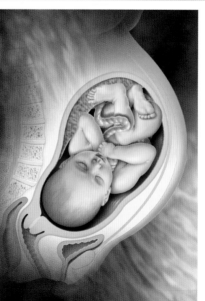

susan leopold

representatives
patricia lindgren
piper smith
tricia weber

new york 212.397.7330
san francisco 415.788.8552
online portfolio at
www.lindgrensmith.com

francis livingston

representatives

patricia lindgren

piper smith

tricia weber

new york 212.397.7330

san francisco 415.788.8552

online portfolio at

www.lindgrensmith.com

bill mayer

representatives
patricia lindgren
piper smith
tricia weber

new york 212.397.7330
san francisco 415.788.8552
online portfolio at
www.lindgrensmith.com

We go together

Waiting Room

lindgren & smith

joe & kathy heiner

representatives
patricia lindgren
piper smith
tricia weber

new york 212.397.7330
san francisco 415.788.8552
online portfolio at
www.lindgrensmith.com

matsu

representatives

patricia lindgren

piper smith

tricia weber

new york 212.397.7330

san francisco 415.788.8552

online portfolio at

www.lindgrensmith.com

Open All Night

lindgrensmith.com

stephan daigle	rick peterson
joseph fiedler	bruno paciulli
doug fraser	chuck pyle
joe & kathy heiner	deborah racer
martin haake	tim raglin
jennifer herbert	robert rodriguez
miles hyman	steven salerno
jeff jackson	valerie sinclair
kim johnson	valerie sokolova
susan leopold	robert gantt steele
francis livingston	mary thelen
lori lohstoeter	bethann thornburgh
bill mayer	pol turgeon
matsu	stefano vitale
jonny mendelsson	cynthia von buhler
yan nascimbene	robert wagt
chris o'leary	jean wisenbaugh
michael paraskevas	brian zick

lindgren & smith ✩ new york 212.397.7330 ✩ san francisco 415.788.8552

NATIONAL ASSOCIATION FOR SPECIALTY FOOD TRADE

Bryan LEISTER
www.bryanleister.com

GEORGETOWN UNIVERSITY BUSINESS MAGAZINE

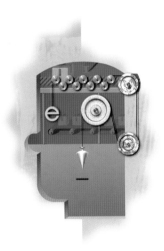

SHOSTAK DESIGN / CEO MAGAZINE

THE MAGAZINE GROUP / FEDERAL CATALYST MAGAZINE

SHOSTAK DESIGN / CEO MAGAZINE

JACQUELINE DeDELL

INTERNAL AUDITOR MAGAZINE

*Mick*WIGGINS
www.mickwiggins.com

362

RANSCOMBE COMPANY/WORKOPOLIS

JOHN HANCOCK FUNDS

RANSCOMBE COMPANY/WORKOPOLIS

JACQUELINE DEDELL Inc

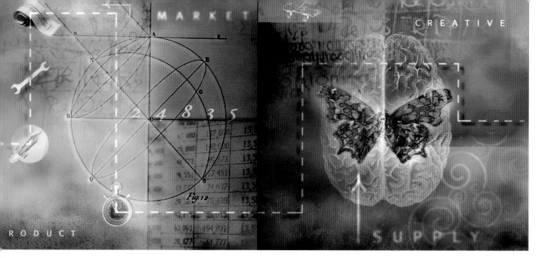

HARVARD BUSINESS REVIEW

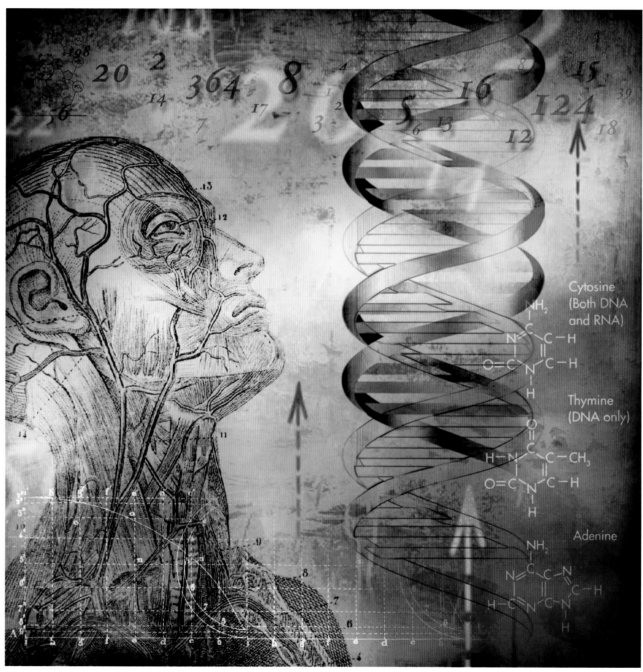

MANAGED CARE MAGAZINE

Alicia BUELOW
www.aliciabuelow.com

MACWORLD MAGAZINE

CMP, WEB TECHNIQUES MAGAZINE

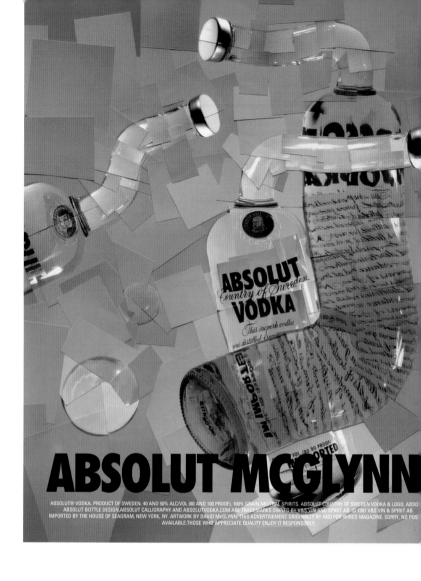

ABSOLUT MCGLYNN

David McGLYNN
www.davidmcglynn.com

JACQUELINE DEDELL Inc.

RED HERRING

JACQUELINE DeDELL *Inc*

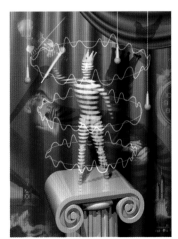

NEW YORK TIMES

COMMVERGE

FRONTIER

www.kellybrother.com

HOUGHTON MIFFLIN PUBLISHERS

BUSINESSWEEK

MADISON SQUARE GARDEN CORPORATION

THE DAILY TELEGRAPH MAGAZINE/UK

GARDENS ILLUSTRATED (UK)

GARDENS ILLUSTRATED (UK)

WINDSTAR CRUISES

WINDSTAR CRUISES

www.christophercorr.com

JACQUELINE DEDELL Inc

GRAND OHIO

MOTIVE POWER MURAL

PITTSBURGH FEDERAL HOME LOAN BANK

JACQUELINE DEDELL

Inc

DONNA IN FORMA

DONNA MODERNA

ARTI GRAFICHE MERONI

DONNA MODERNA

DALLAS MORNING NEWS

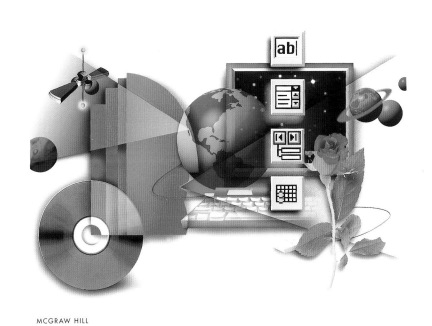

MCGRAW HILL

JACQUELINE DEDELL Inc

NORTH CASTLE DESIGN

WAMSO

MARSHALL FIELD'S

JACQUELINE DEDELL 58 WEST 15TH STREET, NEW YORK, NY, 10011 **TEL:** (212) 741-2539 **FAX:** (212) 741-4660
www.jdedell.com   www.theispot.com

376

LUMINEX

HELPS PREVENT DATA DECAY

INFOTRIEVER

USA WEEKEND

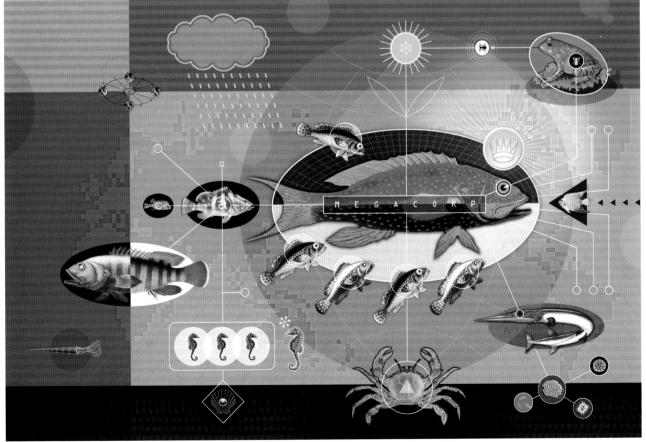

BUSINESS WEEK

JACQUELINE DEDELL inc.

NATIONAL FOOTBALL LEAGUE

EQUAL OPPORTUNITY MAGAZINE

THE AMERICAN SPECTATOR

JACQUELINE DEDELL *Inc.*

IEEE COMPUTER SOCIETY

E WEEK

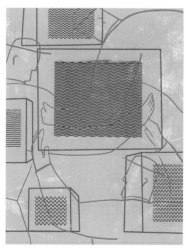

CAHNERS MAGAZINE

BUSINESS WEEK

HERMAN MILLER

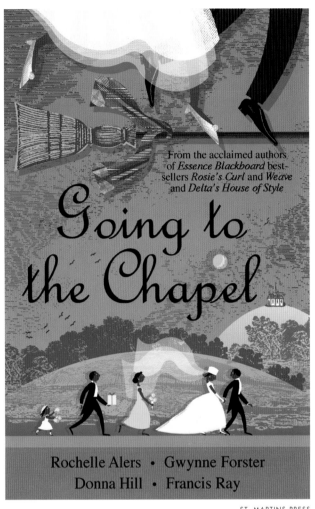

From the acclaimed authors
of *Essence Blackboard* best-
sellers *Rosie's Curl* and *Weave*
and *Delta's House of Style*

Going to the Chapel

Rochelle Alers • Gwynne Forster
Donna Hill • Francis Ray

ST. MARTINS PRESS

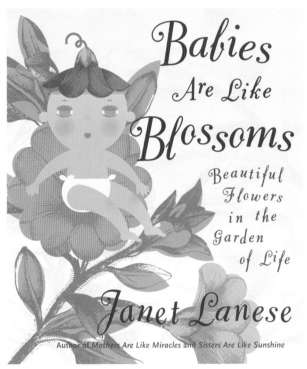

Babies Are Like Blossoms

Beautiful Flowers in the Garden of Life

Janet Lanese

Author of *Mothers Are Like Miracles* and *Sisters Are Like Sunshine*

SIMON & SCHUSTER

HARCOURT BRACE

JACQUELINE DeDELL *Inc*

Debbie Hanley

Daisy Art Studio
500 Aurora Ave N #405
Seattle, WA 98109
fone/phax: (206) 621-0410
www.daisyartstudio.com

Jan Collier

Represents

ASTONISHING FACTS. EXQUISITE ART.

> See all the Workbooks ever printed.
> And Alt Pick.
> And www.jan-collier-represents.com

> Gary Baseman
> Richard Borge
Gerald Bustamante
Rae Ecklund
Brett Emanuel
> Joe Fleming
Travis Foster
Tyson Fuller
Elliott Golden
David Lesh
Greg Mably
David Milgrim
> Christian Northeast
Jennie Oppenheimer
Marti Somers
Peter Sylvada
> Mark Todd
> Esther Pearl Watson
> Nicholas Wilton

TEL 415.383.9026
FAX 415.383.9037
EMAIL jan@jan-collier-represents.com

www.jan-collier-represents.com

Mark Todd

Represented by Jan Collier (415) 383-9026 (415) 383-9037 fax www.jan-collier-represents.com

Gary Baseman

Represented by Jan Collier (415) 383-9026 (415) 383-9037 fax www.jan-collier-represents.com
Editorial (323) 934-5567 (323) 934-5516 fax

Gary Baseman Represented by Jan Collier (415) 383-9026 (415) 383-9037 fax www.jan-collier-represents.com
Editorial (323) 934-5567 (323) 934-5516 fax

Joe Fleming

Represented by Jan Collier (415) 383-9026 (415) 383-9037 fax www.jan-collier-represents.com

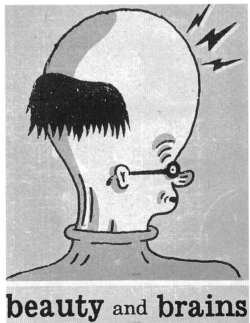

Christian Northeast

Esther Pearl Watson

Represented by Jan Collier (415) 383-9026 (415) 383-9037 fax www.jan-collier-represents.com

Nicholas Wilton

Represented by Jan Collier (415) 383-9026 (415) 383-9037 fax www.jan-collier-represents.com
www.zocolo.com

WPP Group Annual Report, *The numbers in full* (above)　　Inc. Magazine, *Patent Thieves* (right)

Callaway Golf Balls, *Hang time*

Richard Borge

Represented by Jan Collier (415) 383-9026 (415) 383-9037 fax www.jan-collier-represents.com
Editorial assignments (212) 262-9823 **richardborge.com**

TWA Magazine, *Chasing the MP3 factory*

Richard Borge   Represented by Jan Collier (415) 383-9026 (415) 383-9037 fax www.jan-collier-represents.com
Editorial assignments (212) 262-9823 **richardborge.com**

Levy Creative Management
tel: {212} 687 6463
fax: {212} 661 4839
www.levycreative.com
info@levycreative.com

Jenny Laden

Levy Creative Management
tel: {212} 687-6463
fax: {212} 661-4839
www.levycreative.com
info@levycreative.com

Roberto Parada

Levy Creative Management
tel: {212} 687-6463
fax: {212} 661-4839
www.levycreative.com
info@levycreative.com

Lauren Redniss

Levy Creative Management
tel: {212} 687-6463
fax: {212} 661-4839
www.levycreative.com
info@levycreative.com

Jonathan Weiner

Levy Creative Management
tel: {212} 687-6463
fax: {212} 661-4839
www.levycreative.com
info@levycreative.com

L

Thomas Fluharty

Levy Creative Management
tel: {212} 687-6463
fax: {212} 661-4839
www.levycreative.com
info@levycreative.com

Levy Creative Management
tel: {212} 687-6463
fax: {212} 661-4839
www.levycreative.com
info@levycreative.com

Tim Okamura

Levy Creative Management
tel: {212} 687-6463
fax: {212} 661-4839
www.levycreative.com
info@levycreative.com

Max Grafe

Levy Creative Management
tel: {212} 687-6463
fax: {212} 661-4839
www.levycreative.com
info@levycreative.com

Oren Sherman

Levy Creative Management
tel: {212} 687-6463
fax: {212} 661-4839
www.levycreative.com
info@levycreative.com

Alan Dingman

Levy Creative Management
tel: {212} 687-6463
fax: {212} 661-4839
www.levycreative.com
info@levycreative.com

Levy Creative Management
tel: {212} 687-6463
fax: {212} 661-4839
www.levycreative.com
info@levycreative.com

M I C H A E L   I N G L E
I L L U S T R A T I O N

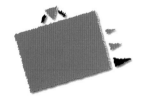

THE NEIS GROUP
ILLUSTRATION • DESIGN • PHOTOGRAPHY

11440 OAK DRIVE • P.O. BOX 174 • SHELBYVILLE, MICHIGAN 49344
TELEPHONE 616-672-5756 • FAX 616-672-5757 • www.neisgroup.com

Compuware Corporation

"Falling Water"

Compuware Corporation

Consumers Energy

MATT LeBARRE

I L L U S T R A T I O N

THE NEIS GROUP

ILLUSTRATION • DESIGN • PHOTOGRAPHY

11440 OAK DRIVE • P.O. BOX 174 • SHELBYVILLE, MICHIGAN 49344
TELEPHONE 616-672-5756 • FAX 616-672-5757 • www.neisgroup.com

GMAC Canada Advantage

Cover illustration from Saving Ben, a Books for All Learners title published by Harcourt School Publishers. Copyright © by Harcourt, Inc.

Daimler Chrysler Corporation

ERIKA LeBARRE
ILLUSTRATION

THE NEIS GROUP
ILLUSTRATION • DESIGN • PHOTOGRAPHY

11440 OAK DRIVE • P.O. BOX 174 • SHELBYVILLE, MICHIGAN 49344
TELEPHONE 616-672-5756 • FAX 616-672-5757 • www.neisgroup.com

Do your clients deserve more than

stock solutions?

We think so.

Original ideas deserve *original art.*

Representing

george abe = www.georgeabe.com

don baker = www.don-baker.com

margaret chodos-irvine = www.chodos-irvine.com

tom collicott = www.tomcollicott.com

stephanie dalton cowan = www.daltoncowan.com

brant day = www.brantday.com

hilber nelson = www.hilbernelson.com

riccardo stampatori = www.riccardostampatori.com

suling wang = www.best.com/~sulingw/illustrations.html

KOLEA BAKER ARTIST REPRESENTATIVE = *206-784-1136* *www.kolea.com*

Original Ideas Deserve Original Art

phone 206.784.1136   www.kolea.com   www.hilbernelson.com

stephanie **dalton cowan**

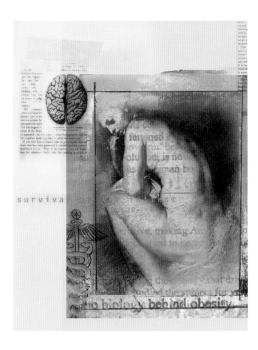

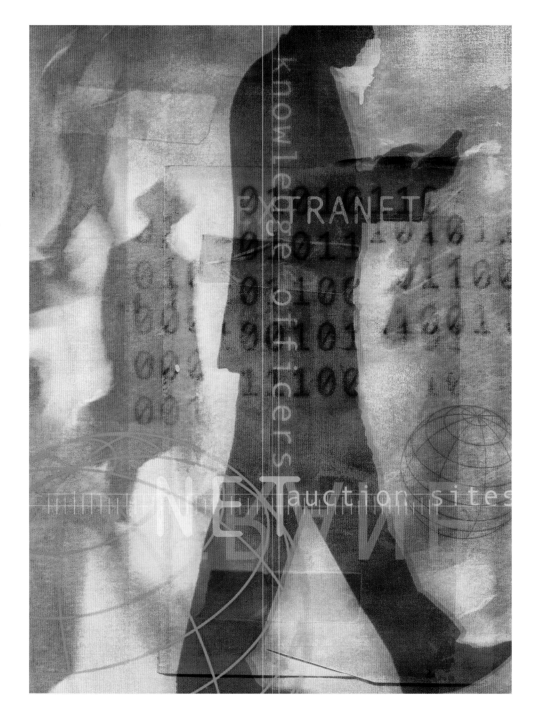

george abe

margaret chodos-irvine

Washington Council for the Humanities "Insomnia"

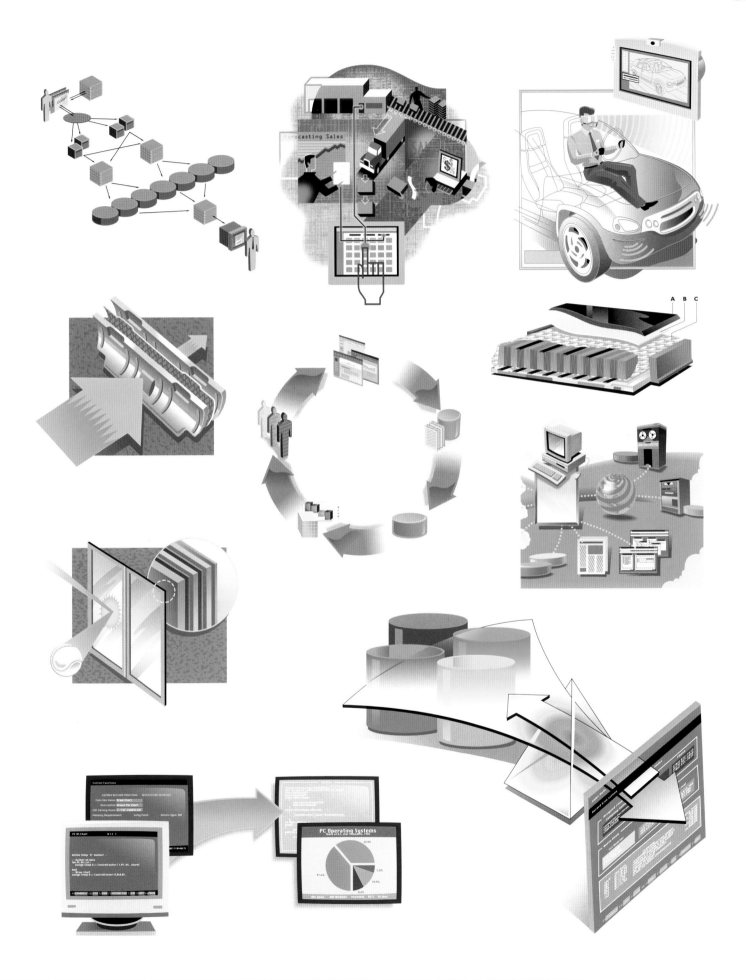

RON CHAN

JEFFREY PELO

BUZZ

415.441.4384

BUD PEEN

TIMOTHY COOK

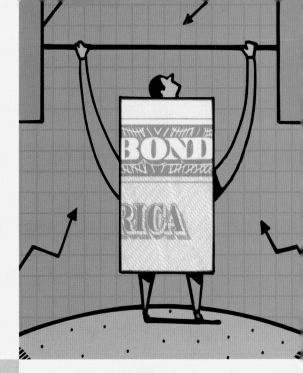

GORDON STUDER

RANDY LYHUS

BUZZ
BUZZILLO.COM

BECKY HEAVNER

GLENN MITSUI

TIMOTHY COOK

PHONE 301.949.5002   FAX 301.949.5003

WEB TIMOTHYCOOK.COM (PORTFOLIO + SEARCHABLE STOCK CATALOG)

TIMOTHY COOK   PHONE 301.949.5002   FAX 301.949.5003

WEB TIMOTHYCOOK.COM

BUZZ
415.441.4384
BUZZILLO.COM

Randy Lyhus

phone 301.986.0036
fax 301.907.4653

www.randylyhus.com

Search from over 600 stock images online.

GORDON STUDER +

freedom

variety

change

5°

five

magnetic

666

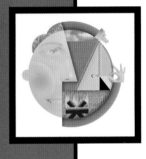

EXTRA!
EXTRA!

To see more images, view our online portfolio, stock and web animation at : www.gordonstuder.com. Also visit www.monsterillo.com and www.buzzillo.com.

gstuder@dnai.com

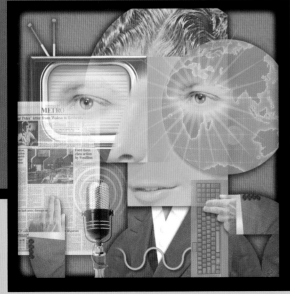

510.655.4256
www.gordonstuder.com

B U Z Z
415.441.4384
BUZZILLO.COM

GLENN MITSUI
ILLUSTRATION

www.glennmitsui.com | glenn@glennmitsui.com | 206.283.5901 | cell: 206.619.9403
fax: 425.687.0113 | 557 roy street, suite 150 seattle wa. 98109

Darwin Magazine

PCWorld Magazine

WallStreet Journa

GLENN MITSUI
ILLUSTRATION

www.glennmitsui.com | glenn@glennmitsui.com | 206.283.5901 | cell: 206.619.9403
fax: 425.687.0113 | 557 roy street, suite 150 seattle wa. 98109

tony gable & 206 cd cover

Axis

USAid

BUZZ
415.441.4384
BUZZILLO.COM

Becky Heavner

tel 703.683.1544
fax 703.683.0872

Keyword search through
hundreds of my stock images at
www.beckyheavner.com

SEARCH MY ONLINE STOCK DATABASE

RON@RONCHAN.COM

415:389:6549

USA TODAY

BID4REAL.COM

CHIEF EXECUTIVE GUIDE

ronchan.com

CALIFORNIA REAL ESTATE MAGAZINE

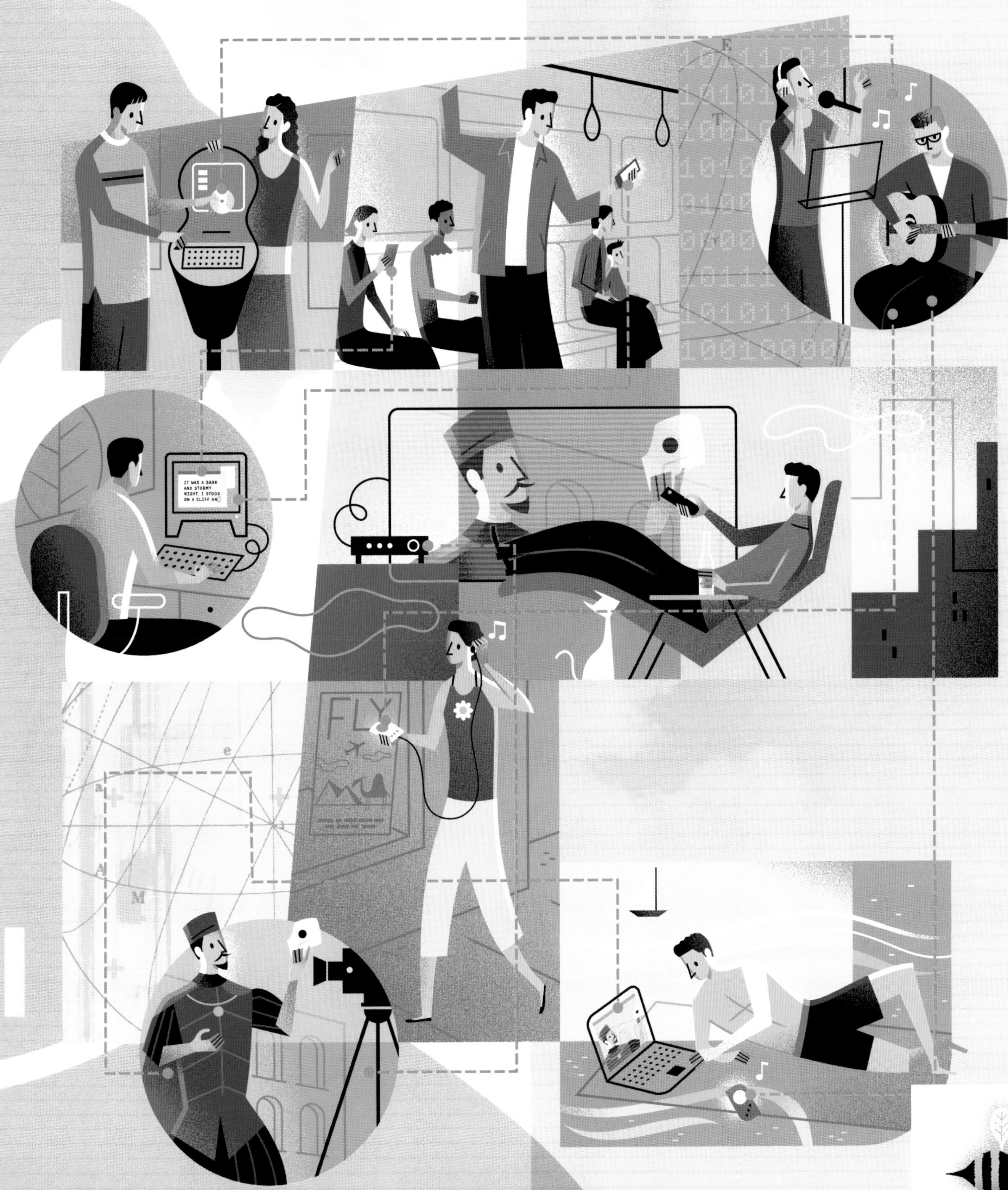
IT WAS A DARK
AND STORMY
NIGHT. I STOOD
ON A CLIFF AN
FLY

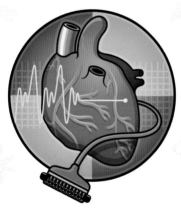

JE PELO
PELO

415·388·2076
WWW.JEFFREYPELO.COM

BUZZ
415.441.4384
BUZZILLO.COM

433

Art*works*®

representing

paul **bachem**

kim **barnes**

dan **brown**

harry **burman**

deborah **chabrian**

ellis **chappell**

adrian **chesterman**

christopher b. **clarke**

bob **dombrowski**

daniel **mark duffy**

peter **fiore**

stephen **gardner**

mike **harper**

rick **lovell**

dennis **lyall**

molly **o'gorman**

larry **schwinger**

peter **siu**

brad **teare**

jerry **vanderstelt**

victoria **vebell**

212.239.4946

325 West 38 Street Suite 1605 NYC 10018

Contact Betty Krichman or Ron Puhalski

T 212.239.4946 F 212.239.6106

E artworksillustration@earthlink.net

W www.artworksillustration.com

To see more images visit us at
theispot.com/rep/artworksillustration.com.

jerry **vanderstelt**

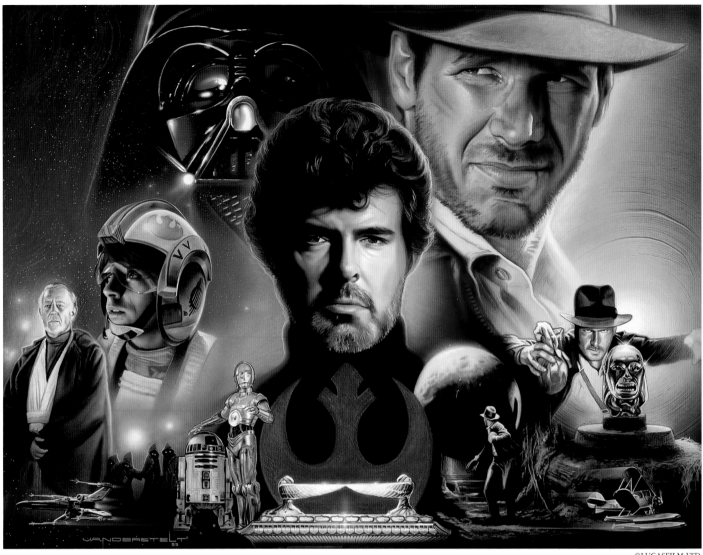

325 West 38 Street Suite 1605 New York City 10018 Contact Betty Krichman or Ron Puhalski
T 212.239.4946 F 212.239.6106 E artworksillustration@earthlink.net W www.artworksillustration.com
To see more images visit us at theispot.com/rep/artworksillustration.com

jerry **vanderstelt**

dan **brown**

peter **fiore**

 **Art** *works*®

325 West 38 Street Suite 1605 New York City 10018 Contact Betty Krichman or Ron Puhalski
T 212.239.4946 F 212.239.6106 E artworksillustration@earthlink.net W www.artworksillustration.com
To see more images visit us at theispot.com/rep/artworksillustration.com

adrian **chesterman**

kim **barnes**

rick **lovell**

mike **harper**

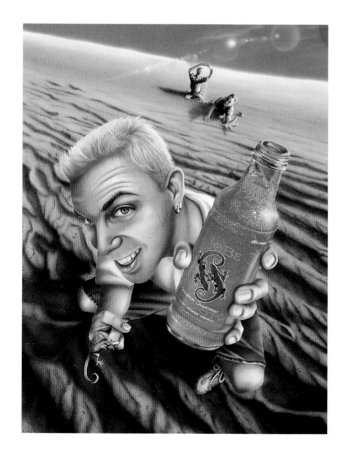

325 West 38 Street Suite 1605 New York City 10018 Contact Betty Krichman or Ron Puhalski
T 212.239.4946 F 212.239.6106 E artworksillustration@earthlink.net W www.artworksillustration.com
To see more images visit us at theispot.com/rep/artworksillustration.com

peter **siu**

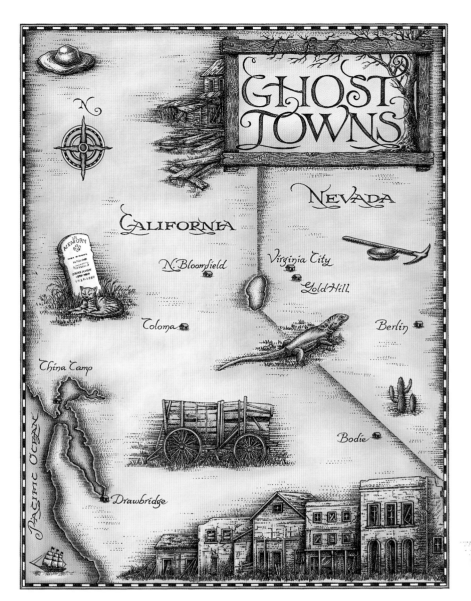

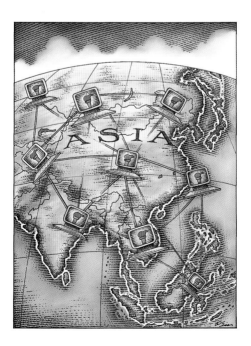

paul **bachem**

dennis **lyall**

deborah **chabrian**

christopher b. **clarke**

stephen **gardner**

325 West 38 Street Suite 1605 New York City 10018 Contact Betty Krichman or Ron Puhalski
T 212.239.4946 F 212.239.6106 E artworksillustration@earthlink.net W www.artworksillustration.com
To see more images visit us at theispot.com/rep/artworksillustration.com

444

Anita Grien
155 East 38th Street
New York, NY 10016
tel (212) 697-6170
fax (212) 697-6177
www.anitagrien.com

Julie Johnson
Represented by Anita Grien

Digital and Traditional Art

The 2000 International Beauty Show

College of Medicine, University of Iowa

Make the Connection
by Oprah Winfrey
(Hyperion)

JIM CHOW

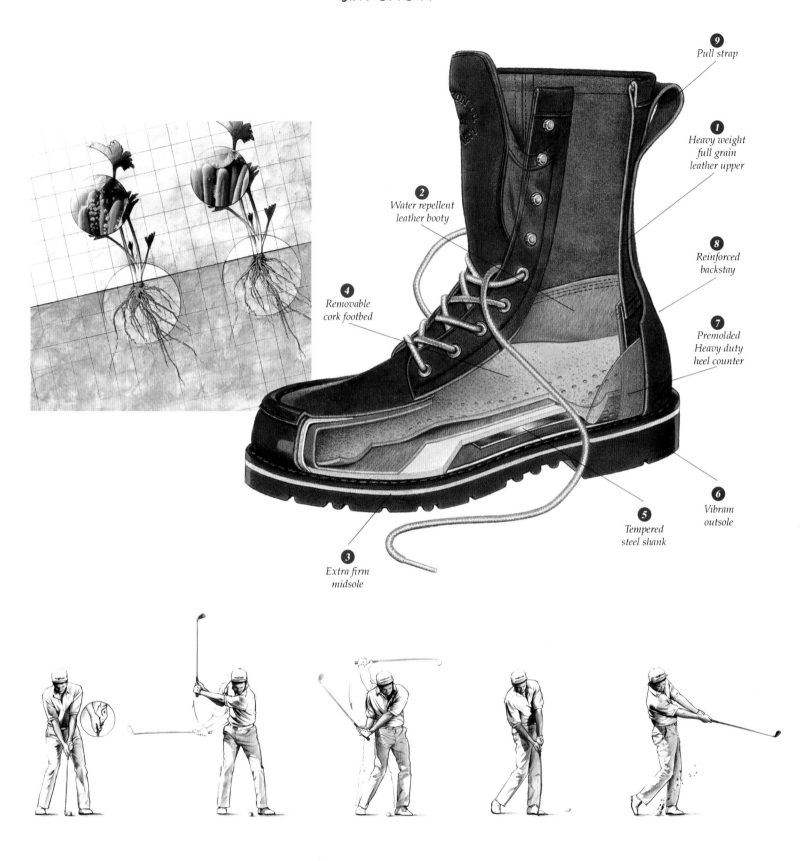

9 *Pull strap*

1 *Heavy weight full grain leather upper*

2 *Water repellent leather booty*

8 *Reinforced backstay*

4 *Removable cork footbed*

7 *Premolded Heavy duty heel counter*

6 *Vibram outsole*

5 *Tempered steel shank*

3 *Extra firm midsole*

FON: 303-820-2599 • FAX: 303-820-2598 • TOLL : 1-800-417-5120

artagent.com

RANDY ZWINGLER

| cartoons | illustration | 3d | logos + ikons | animation | contact |

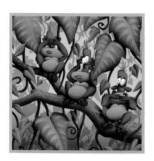

*See more art online at
www.artagent.com/ward*

Character animation in Flash

CAROL GUENZI AGENTS
WWW.ARTAGENT.COM

FON: 303-820-2599 • FAX: 303-820-2598 • TOLL : 1-800-417-5120
www.artagent.com

CHRISTER ERIKSSON

JOE McDERMOTT

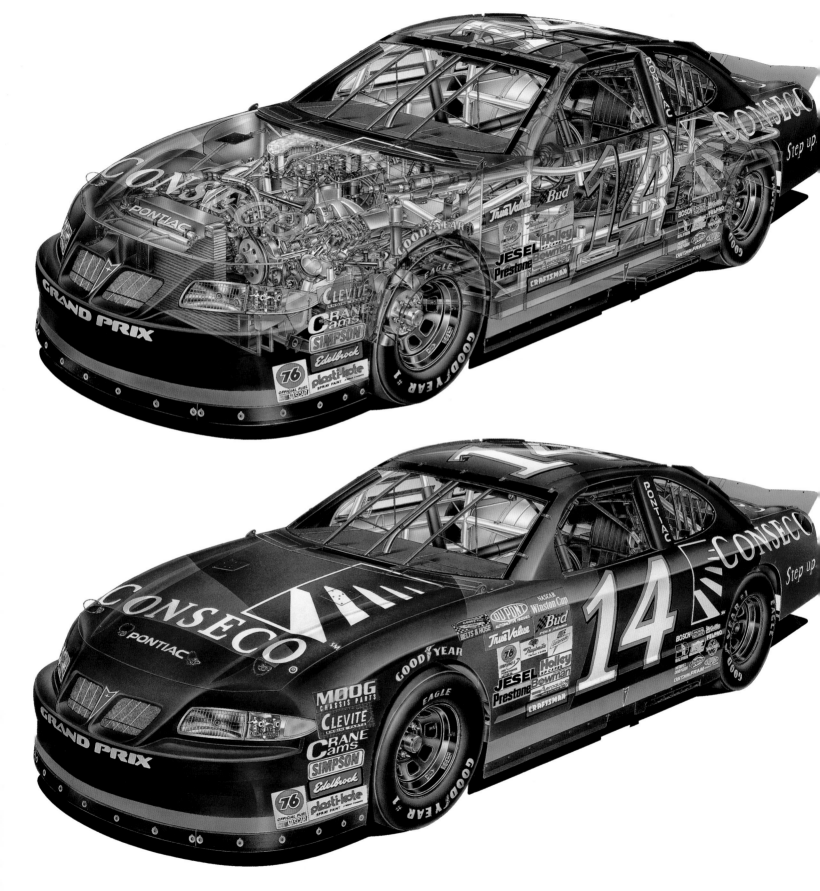

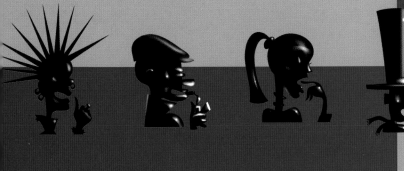

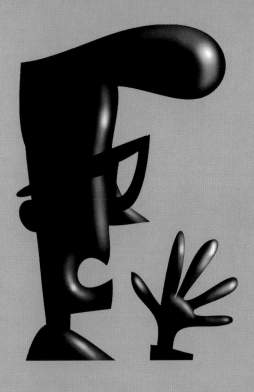

ADAM McCAULEY
PORTFOLIO ONE

REPRESENTED BY ⁓ **MASLOV WEINBERG** 415.641.1285
ATOMICALLEY.COM ⁓ EDITORIAL/STUDIO **510.832.0860**

MASLOV & WEINBERG ★ 608 YORK STREET ★ SAN FRANCISCO. CA 94110 ★ PHONE 415.641.1285 ★ FAX 415.641.5500

John Gilbert

Tom Mix

Mark

REPRES

Maslov

Sa

★

TODAY'S
OF THE S

Theda Bara

Roscoe Arbuckle

Conrad Veidt

Lupe Velez

Matcho

TED BY

Weinberg

tes

OP STARS

ER SCREEN

★

Anna Mae Wong

Wallace Beery

MARK MATCHO • 70 HARKNESS AVENUE #9 • PASADENA, CA 91106 • PHONE 626.796.6906 • FAX 626.796.9640 • MARKMATCHO@AOL.COM

scotthull.com

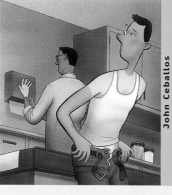 John Ceballos

 John Patrick

 Andrew Lewis

 Larry Moore

 Stephen Schudlich

 Mark Riedy

wehavecomeofage

scott hull
assoc inc

headquarters
937 433.8383

facsimile
937 433.0434

new york
212 966.3604

san fransisco
415 285.3808

 Jon Lezinsky

 Doug Fryer

new

 turnstyle
by Scott Hull Associates

fresh ideas.
simple term

 Andrea Eberbach

 Clint Hansen

 Andy Buttram

 Young-Min Yoon

 Tracy Britt

 Aimee Sicuro

Larry Moore

John Maggard

Noma

Andy Powell

David Bowers

Geoff Smith

turnstyle

by Scott Hull Associates

fresh ideas.
simple terms.

new

Greg Dearth

Curtis Parker

Jeffrey Stemen

Young Sook Cho

Andrew Lewis

Andrea Eberbach

Lorraine Tuson

Greg LaFever

**scott
hull**
*assoc
inc*

headquarters
937 433.8383

facsimile
937 433.0434

new york
212 966.3604

san fransisco
415 285.3808

wehavecomeofage

scotthull.com

STEPHEN SCHUDLICH

"i'm allergic to horses."

Quite Possibly The Fastest Illustrator In The West.

David Bowers. b Chambersburg, PA, 1956.   **The Bird King.**   2000.   Oil on masonite.   **h** 15½ x **w** 10¼ in.   Private Collection

Ty Wilson

Monica Lind

Andrew Mockett

Dan Cotton

Telephone 212.431.4480

Fax 212.253.9996

Web watsonspierman.com

Watson & Spierman

Telephone 212.431.4480 **Web** watsonspierman.com

Kim Harlow

Tim Barrall

Fulvia Zambon

Annabelle Verhoye

COREY
represents
graham

frank ansley

andrea brooks

kirk caldwell

tim clark

jon conrad

zoe danae falliers

jim dandy

giles hancock

ken jacobsen

joel nakamura

michael nelson

ken orvidas

nicolas pavloff

william rieser

david tillinghast

robin zingone

COREY graham
PIER 33 NORTH
san francisco 94111
TEL: 415.956.4750   FAX: 415.391.6104
www.coreygrahamreps.com

Joel Nakamura
Paintings and Illustrations

Tecate Beer

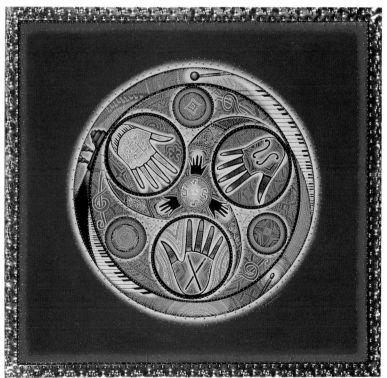

Chick Corea   New Trio

Studio
505   989-1404

Web
www.joelnakamura.com

REP
Corey Graham   415   956-4750

DAVID TILLINGHAST

www.davidtillinghast.com

DAVID TILLINGHAST

www.davidtillinghast.com

PHONE : 323-256-3065

1300 YOSEMITE DRIVE • LOS ANGELES • CA • 90041   FAX: 323-256-3066

REPRESENTED ON THE WEST COAST BY COREY GRAHAM REPRESENTS 415-956-4750

WWW.COREYGRAHAMREPS.COM   WWW.WORKBOOK.COM   E-MAIL: CGR2@MINDSPRING.COM

www.whydandy.com

Jim Dandy

jim dandy is represented by corey graham in san francisco / 415.956.4750 / www.coreygrahamreps.com
editorial assignments call jim dandy @ 480-829-8992 / www.whydandy.com

TIM CLARK

ILLUSTRATION
STUDIO

timoclark@earthlink.net

represented by **Corey Graham**

tel. 415 956 4750

888 202 8091

fax 415 391 6104

cgr2@mindspring.com

www.coreygrahamreps.com

check out www.theispot.com

JAMES YANG / www.jamesyang.com Represented By DAVID GOLDMAN AGENCY
41 Union Square West, Suite 918, New York, NY 10003
Ph: 212-807-6627 FAX: 212-463-8175 www.davidgoldmanagency.com

DININNO

STEVE DININNO/ www.stevedininno.com is Represented By DAVID GOLDMAN AGENCY
41 Union Square West, Suite 918, New York, NY 10003
Ph: 212-807-6627 FAX: 212-463-8175 www.davidgoldmanagency.com

Nishan

NISHAN AKGULIAN/ www.nishanakgulian.com is Represented By **DAVID GOLDMAN AGENCY**
41 Union Square West, Suite 918, New York, NY 10003
Ph: 212-807-6627 FAX: 212-463-8175 www.davidgoldmanagency.com

BENDELL

NORM BENDELL is Represented By DAVID GOLDMAN AGENCY
41 Union Square West, Suite 918, New York, NY 10003
Ph: 212-807-6627 FAX: 212-463-8175 www.davidgoldmanagency.com

seeing
RED
beauty

PERC

FR

COL

TAL

IMAGI

fire

HOT

animal

air

feathers

FO
WL

devil

DARKNESS

CHAOS

IRMELI
HOLMBERG

TEL 212 545 9155

FAX 212 545 9462

IRMELI@AOL.COM

280 MADISON AVENUE

NEW YORK NY 10016

CAROLYN HOLMAN

ROB JOHNSON

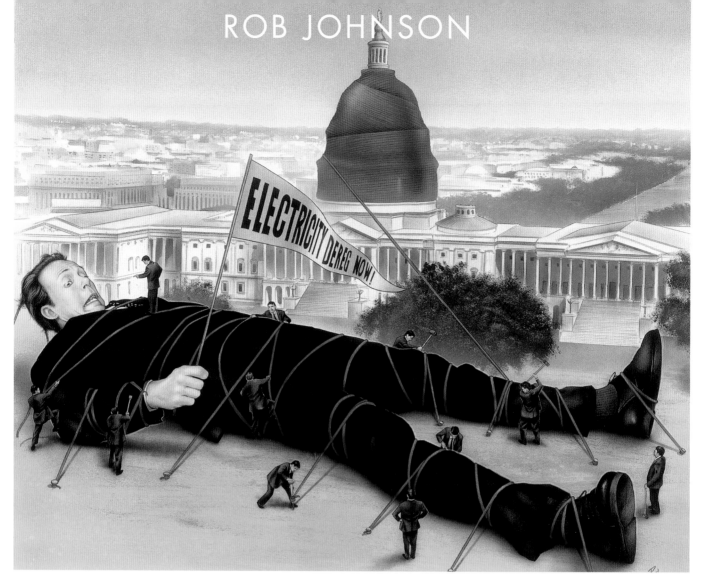

Bruce MacPherson

A

Illustration & Surface Design
Lilla Rogers Studio

www.lillarogers.com >> 781 641 2787 >> info@lillarogers.c

C

C Maria Carluccio
D Greg Morgan

LET STARBUCKS COFFEE TAKE YOU THERE

B

A Sarajo Frieden
B Jon Cannell

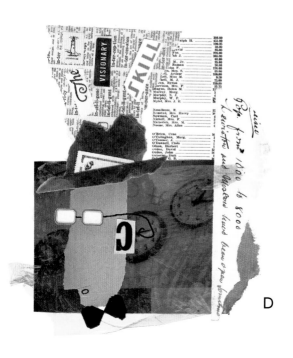

D

Elizabethan Lady wearing fashion...

F

spur metabolism

R

83% of angina patients still experience angina pain.

therapeutic

angina

RANOLAZINE, potentially the first in a new class of drugs called partial fatty acid oxidation (pFOX) inhibitors, is being developed for the potential treatment of chronic angina. UNMET NEED: The wrenching pain of angina occurs when obstructions in the coronary arteries deprive the heart of the oxygenated

G

H

www.lillarogers.com >> 781 641 2787 >> info@lillarogers.com

I

J

M

K

L

Ɛ,F	Susan McKenna
G	Anne Smith
H	Diane Bigda
I	Sarajo Frieden
J	Ann Boyajian
K	Susy Pilgrim Waters
L	Susan Farrington
M	Janell Genovese

Illustration & Surface Design

Lilla Rogers Studio

www.lillarogers.com >> 781 641 2787 >> info@lillarogers.com

representing **Linda Ketelhut**

I'm always up for it so blast my Agent an E'mail
and I'll reply personally. Due to the wonders of the
latest technology and the time difference, you can
brief me at 5 o'clock you will have something to look
at with your morning coffee.
The bonus is that you will find we are cheaper over here too.
Founded as an artist co-operative.

Advocate,
372 Old York Road,
London SW18 1SP

Tel: +44 (0)208 877 0072 Fax: +44 (0)208 874 7661
Web : www.advocate-art.com E-Mail : mail@advocate-art.com
Representing 60 exclusive and over 100 associate artists.

ADVOCATE   Peter Greenwood

Christian Birmingham

Sarah Gibb

THEARTWORKS USA

Carla Siboldi

Anthony Russo

Greg Clarke

Penny Dann

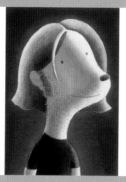

Marcin Baranski

Rutu Modan

CHICAGO
t (312) 372 8081
f (312) 372 8082
Midwest, South
& Southeast

Tatsuro Kiuchi

Charlotte Knox

Douglas Klauba

Sophie Allport

Marco Ventura

Please call the office nearest you
or refer to our website for a more
comprehensive view of our unique
range of talent.

Sarah McMenemy

Robert Shadbolt

Dovrat Ben Nahum

TOKYO
t (813) 379 38691
f (813) 572 21245
Japan
& Pacific Rim

Steve Moors

Jane Watkins

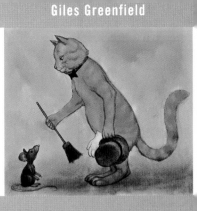

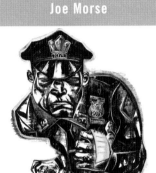

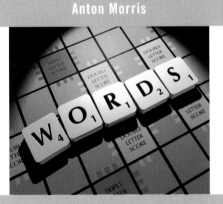

VEGGIE PET

www.danielecollignon-reps.com Studio 1.416.960.3716, winter 1.305.672.3363 or www.billframpton.com or www.theispot.com, or wjframpton@aol.com

Bill Frampton

DAN COSGROVE

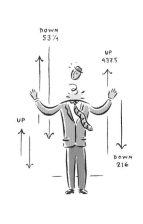

JIM STECK

ERIC BOWMAN

Deborah Melmon

Shelton Leong

Sharon Morris associates | 415.362.8280

artist representative | *fax* 415.362.8310 smasf@aol.com www.sharonartrep.com

Dorothy Remington

Sharon Morris associates | 415.362.8280
artist representative | fax 415.362.8310   smasf@aol.com   www.sharonartrep.com

Illustrator
Dru Blair

Tim Jessell

TEL 918 749 9424   FAX 918 749 5165   www.suzannecraig.com
EAST: STUDIO 405 377 3619   jessell@ionet.net   www.timjessell.com

SUZANNE CRAIG REPRESENTS
INCORPORATED

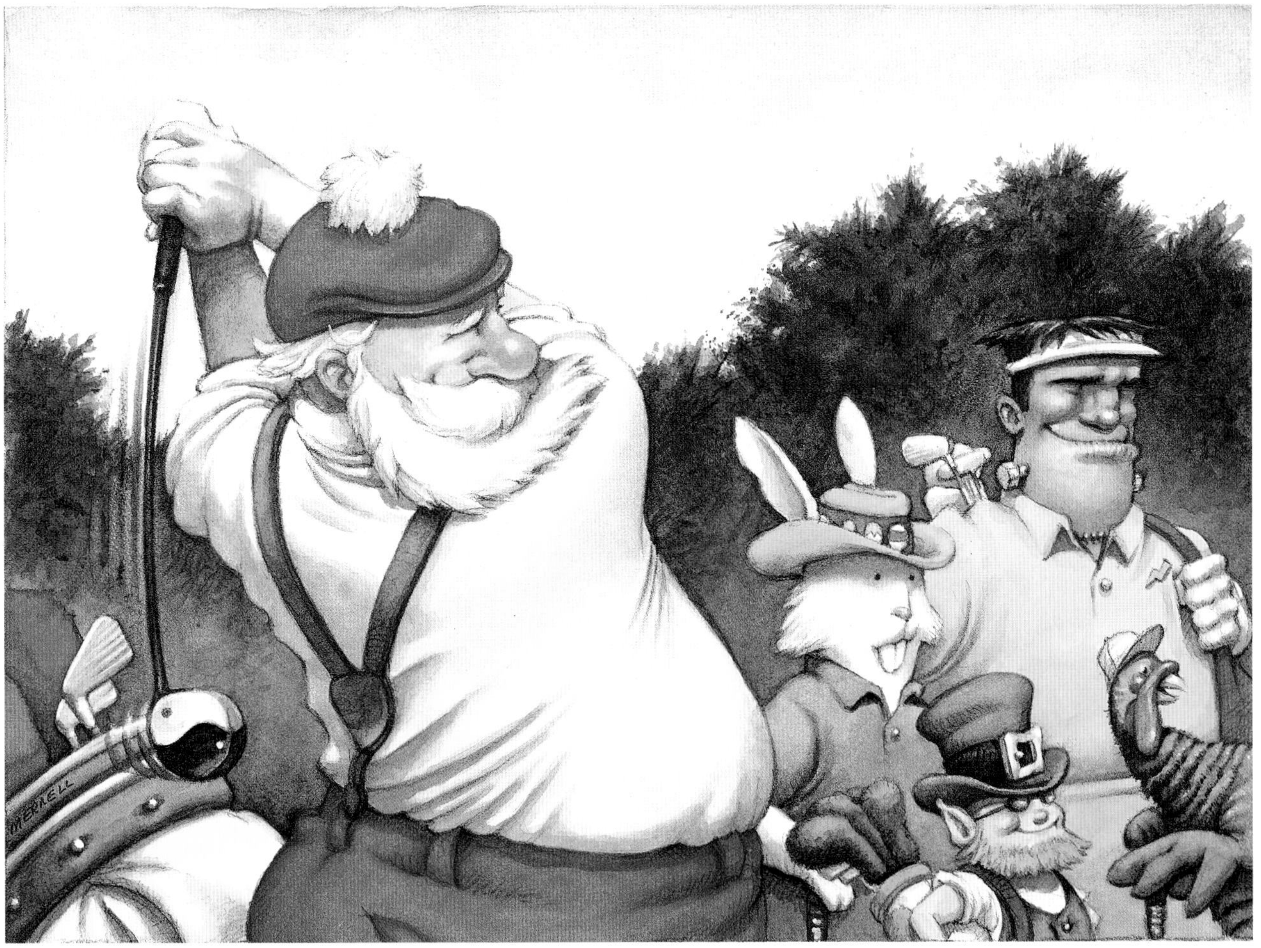

David Webber Merrell

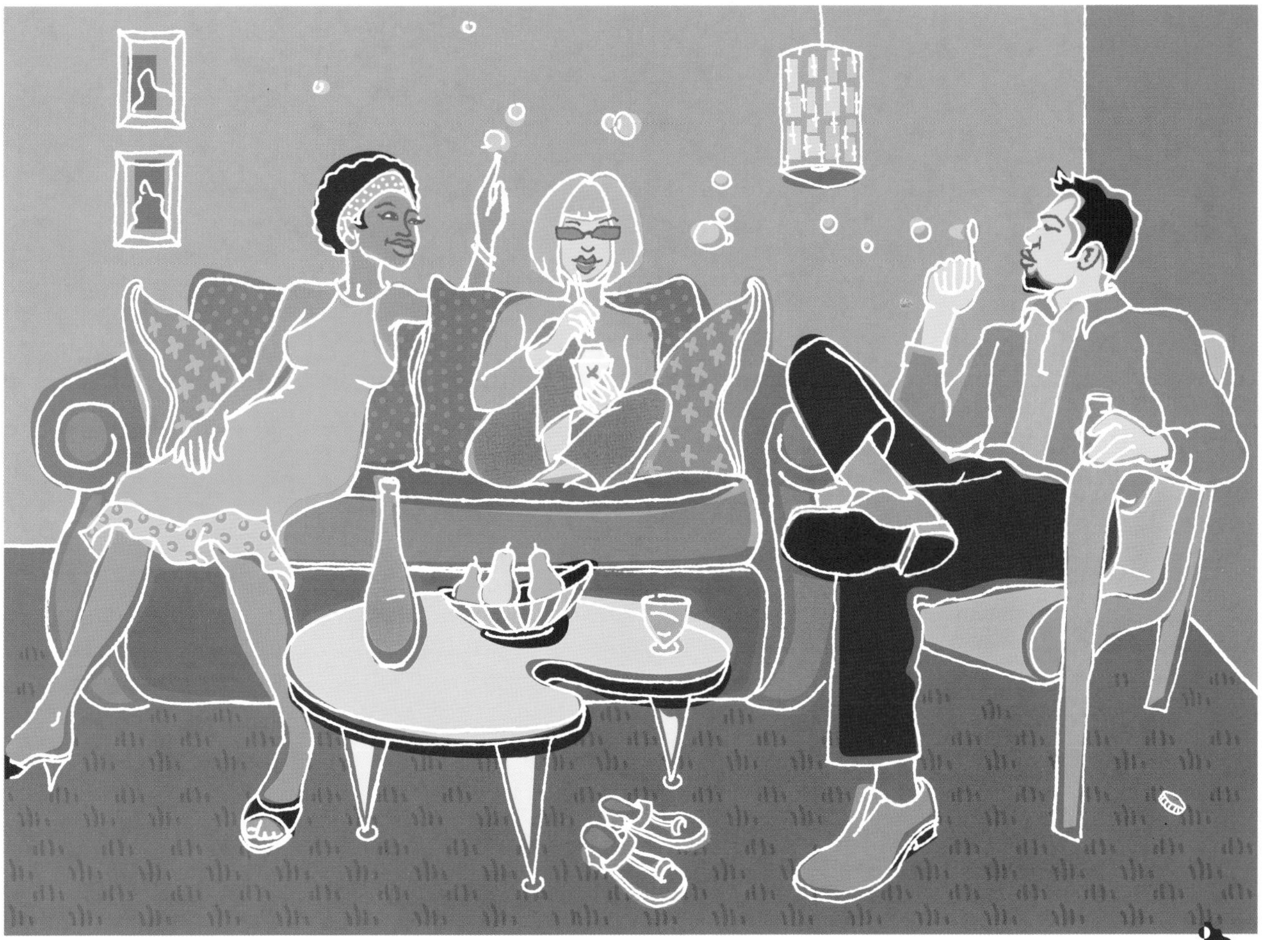

Robin Kachantones

501

Twenty three of the UK's leading humorous and stylized illustrators.

All available online at www.illustratorsdirect.co.uk

With extensive portfolios for each artist, our website is a must-see for art buyers. Go on. Visit the UK with your mouse.

Email splat@illustratorsdirect.co.uk for more information or call Pearl Richardson on 011 44 1325 352446.

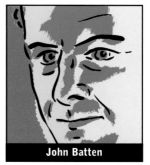
Adrian Barclay

John Batten

Judy Brown

Mike Brownlow

Paul Davies

Trevor Dunton

Kevin Faerber

Paul Hampson

John Haslam

Iain McIntosh

John Blair Moore

Ellis Nadler

Chris Pavely

John Richardson

Mike Roberts

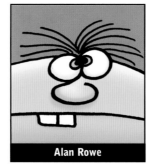
Alan Rowe

Martin Shovel

Dave F Smith

Gary Swift

Kate Taylor

Colin Thompson

Kath Walker

Ian West

www.illustratorsdirect.co.uk

HUMOROUS COMMUNICATIONS

comping is
usage...

please ask first

theispot·showcase™

Better Than Ever...

PORTFOLIOS

STOCK

ABOUT

WHAT'S NEW

Portfolios

See up-to-the-minute work

available 24/7 and only a click away.

Stock Illustrations

Find thousands of quality images

available for immediate electronic delivery.

Virtual Gallery

Add your favorite illustrators' originals

to your personal art collection.

www.the*i*spot.com

e-mail service@theispot.com

toll-free 888.834.7768

index

index

index

index